John Morrison has been a writer for rather longer than he cares to remember. If he'd known how unrewarding the writing game was likely to be, he'd have chosen a more profitable vocation. Like opening a flea circus or running a fried chicken franchise.

He has written almost thirty books, most of which have failed to set the literary world alight. You'll probably know his most recent title: *25 More Walks From Pubs With Warm Beer.* Since he has the priceless gift of being able to laugh at other people's misfortunes, he is now turning to comedy as a way of revitalising a flagging career.

Having moved to the South Pennines he leads a pleasantly informal life, avoiding all activities that require new clothes. He's a sociable guy, and if he had any friends they'd no doubt say the same. He loves mankind, it's just people he can't stand.

His ambition is to establish a relationship more profound than that between a man and his newsagent. And when his time is up he'd like to go in his sleep, like his grandad. Not screaming, like the people in his grandad's car...

Published 1998 by Pennine Pens
Copyright © John Morrison 1998
All rights reserved

ISBN 1 873378 47 5

To D, with love

Cover picture by Andy Hawkins

Typeset and published by Pennine Pens.
32, Windsor Road, Hebden Bridge,
West Yorkshire, HX7 8LF. Tel/Fax 01422-843724
books@penpens.demon.co.uk
http://www.hebdenbridge.co.uk

VIEW FROM THE BRIDGE

John Morrison

Pennine Pens

CONTENTS

Introduction

It's New Years Eve, 1997. From a nearby hilltop you can enjoy a birds-eye view of this little Pennine town, and see just how tightly Milltown is shoehorned into the landscape, hemmed in on all sides by steep hills. There are enough telling clues, within this sweeping panorama, to tell the town's history over the last 500 years.

Above the town are a scattering of farms and their intakes: land won from the moorland and enclosed by a tracery of dry stone walls. Cloth-making helped these upland farmers to survive in the harsh terrain, as spinning and weaving became genuine cottage industries. The handloom weavers lost their independence as their skills began to be mechanised. Small mills were built wherever there was enough running water to turn a waterwheel - in the wooded, steep-sided cloughs around Milltown.

After the introduction of steam power, mills were built in the valley bottom, closer to the roads, the canal and, later, the railway. This is how Milltown grew from a being a mere river-crossing on an ancient packhorse trail to a thriving town, specialising in the production of cotton 'fustian'.

It was while researching a walking book that I first explored this valley. I spent a sunbaked August staggering over vast expanses of moorland, armed with an Ordnance Survey map, a notebook and a tub of foul-smelling insect repellent. On those occasions when the sweat wasn't pouring off my brow and into my eyes, I was enthralled by the views. Every climb up some steep and half-forgotten path would offer a startling new vista to enjoy.

I was intrigued, too, by the proximity of town and country. This, after all, was West Yorkshire: not a part of the country celebrated for its scenic beauty. But the terraced streets backed straight onto open fields; within minutes you could leave the bustle behind and be striding across the moors. Five years later I moved here, into one of the little 'top and bottom' houses that are so typical of the area.

The great days of the textile industries are long gone, and Milltown is just one of many places that went into what must have looked like irreversible decline. But with Nature abhorring a vacuum, Milltown soon filled up again - this time with an intriguingly diverse cast of 'off-cumdens'. Artists, writers, ne'er-do-wells, New-Age therapists, lovers, loners and losers: my kind of people.

This little book began as weekly episodes on the Milltown Web (the town's own lay-by on the information super-highway) in Spring 1997 and covers the nine months that followed. The Milltown Web is a splendid web-site, a labour of love that brings the concerns of this little old milltown to the attention of web-browsers around the world.

The *View From the Bridge* episodes - past, present and future - will remain freely available to anyone with an Internet connection and time hanging heavily on their hands. Just point the browser to... **http://www.hebdenbridge.co.uk**

Or email me... **john@trunorth.demon.co.uk**

John Morrison

1 Springtime in Milltown

S pring has finally arrived in this little old milltown: a great relief for locals driven half crazy by another long Pennine winter. Due to the town's unusual topography, the winter sun seems to set shortly after breakfast. But now the daffodils are out, the trees around the old packhorse bridge are bursting with blossom, and the Town Drunk has come out of hibernation.

Unsteady of gait (buoyed up by a pint of Hammerite and a whisky chaser) and florid of face (sporting the 'corned beef' complexion that drives the women wild) he lurches erratically across the square. He started drinking in order to forget, and has succeeded spectacularly.

It could all have been so very different. As a man of few talents, but almost limitless antagonism towards his fellow man, he could no doubt have been trained to run, say, an angler's bait shop or key-cutting franchise.

If it's true that we get the shops we deserve, then you have to assume that the shopping lists of most people in Milltown feature badly made handicrafts, incense sticks and shapeless sweaters knitted in rainbow colours. "Christ", says Willow Woman, "I'm right out of corn-dollies and hand-dipped candles. Sky, could you nip down to the shops for me?" Her daughter Sky has only recently been diagnosed as suffering from 'Hippy Parent Crap Name Syndrome', and is still smarting from the humiliation. She grinds a dog-end beneath the heel of her Doc Martens and clumps reluctantly down to the shops.

It is one of life's minor mysteries how, in these difficult times, so many shops in Milltown can survive by selling nothing but worthless tat. God only knows what Gerald Ratner would have had to say about the Twig Shop, for example, which is stocked from floor to ceiling with unremarkable items that can be gathered for free from the nearest copse or hedgerow. Apparently sane people are parting with hard-earned cash to buy dried flowers, bent sticks and fir-cones, without having a gun pointed at their heads.

The bookshop, a few doors away, specialises in those arcane titles which have failed, on publication, to set the literary world alight. Their progress from printing press to rubbish skip is interrupted only by a brief sojourn on the 'remaindered' shelves - each volume representing a bizarre aberration of taste or foresight by some overwrought commissioning editor. Which is why the window display is full of titles like *Eat More & Get Slim, The Collectors' Guide to Broken Biscuits* and *The Time-Life Book of Celebrity Breakfasts.*

An attempt by the bookshop to go upmarket was doomed when the local author who came in for a book-signing session resisted the well-meaning advise that he should sign only his *own* books.

It's a mere five-minute walk down to Milltown's cricket pitch, where the team members have assembled after their winter sabbatical. The air is filled with the sounds of the summer game - mostly a hard leather ball colliding with tender, unprotected flesh. The air is full of expectations too: that this year we are finally going to fulfil our obvious cricketing potential, and not continue to be the talent-free embarrassments we've been for as long as anyone can remember.

It is this same kind of unqualified optimism, in the face of all evidence to the contrary, that makes a pavilion full of sodden cricketers gaze across a flooded pitch, where the two sets of stumps are rapidly disappearing beneath the water, and remark, without the slightest hint of irony: "You know, I think it's brightening up".

The smell of new-mown grass is a potent reminder that summer isn't far away, as is the industrial-strength horse liniment that our number five batsman rubs liberally all over himself. As he straps neoprene supports around elbows and knees, he appears to be built out of spare parts from a breaker's yard. He admits to being 55, a figure that's merely a starting point for negotiations.

He is the only member of the team who loosens up before a game, because he is the only member of the team with muscles. He performs inelegant and painful-looking callisthenics while the rest of the team sit around drinking beer and cadging roll-ups. Consequently, he is the only one who ever gets injured: a regular litany of sprains and pulls, requiring yet more liniment and support garments. It's a downward spiral of exercise, injury and visits to the surgical supplies shop that will end - to no-one's great surprise - with him falling to bits altogether.

The long Pennine winters make us think deeply about our place in the cosmos. You wake up in the middle of the night, in a cold sweat. You don't know where you are. You don't even know *who* you are. All you have is a sudden and terrifying comprehension that you are nothing more than a tiny and insignificant cluster of molecules, randomly cast adrift in a vast and uncaring universe. It is this sort of unsettling premonition that makes us question the very nature of existence, or at least vow to stop eating cheese at bedtime.

We don't see many Jehovah's Witnesses in Milltown. These bible-toting teapots know the reception they'll get when they knock on any door. Instead of just telling them to piss off, we invite them in to explain their barmy beliefs in graphic detail. Conditioned to encounter only hostility which, paradoxically, reinforces their special status as the Chosen Ones, they become disorientated by a kind word or welcoming gesture.

The suspension of disbelief is an almost tangible force in Milltown. No faith or creed is too bizarre to gather a handful of committed adherents. If it was suggested, for example, that personal growth might be promoted by standing on your head in a bucket of pig slurry, there'd be one or two undemanding souls who'd nod and say "You know, that makes a lot of sense to me".

Willow Woman, for example, inhabits a convoluted world of pastel colours, in which crystals, mobiles, herbs, astrological charts and inedible home-baked bread play pivotal roles. She asks you what your sign is. "Aries", you reply warily, adding that astrology is a ludicrously random imposition of celestial order that gives comfort only to the most gullible and feeble-minded. Willow Woman gazes back with a countenance so open, honest and guileless that it makes people want to slap some sense into her. "You know", she smiles, somehow managing to combine humility and smugness into a single expression, "a mistrust of astrology is a very Arian characteristic".

So you bite your tongue and refrain from pointing out that when you look at your stars in the papers, they tend to say something anodyne like: "You're going to get a letter this week, meet someone nice, and breathe in and out". What you *don't* see is anything specific, such as: "You are a 31-year-old systems analyst from Cleckheaton, you've got a mole on your left buttock and on Thursday week you are going to have a fatal collision with a bakery truck".

Willow Woman knows the value of everything but the price of nothing. It makes shopping a nightmare. She sorts all her rubbish into different piles for recycling, but never takes them anywhere. Nobody is quite sure where she's from, except that it's a country which shares a common border with Fantasia and Never Never Land. She's only on nodding acquaintance with the real world, and specialises in doomed affairs with utterly inappropriate partners. And every red-blooded male in Milltown would crawl over broken bottles to spend the night with her.

The LETS system of bartering has been adopted enthusiastically by Milltown folk. In an effort to promote a cash-free society (what used to be known, more prosaically, as 'poverty') we exchange our skills and barter our goods. It's a terrific idea, and a cursory glance through the latest bulletin gives a flavour of the enterprise.

Participants list their offers and wants. What people *want* is someone to rewire their house, or mend a clapped-out camper van, or the loan of a Harrier jump-jet for the weekend. What people can *offer* is an unlimited supply of goat's milk, to teach your stressed-out pets to relax, or to lend you a pair of hair clippers. The sharp-eyed reader may spot the fundamental flaw in this arrangement.

We are gearing ourselves up for the General Election; in the streets of Milltown there's an almost palpable air of apathy. Politicians we haven't clapped eyes on for five years are crawling out of the woodwork, happy to do anything - no matter how demeaning - that will win a few extra votes.

Those Tory candidates who can read the writing on the wall are dividing their time between kissing babies and bargaining for highly-paid sinecures with multinational companies. The Liberal Democrats are responding to the by-now traditional exhortation to "Go back to your constituencies and prepare for opposition". Labour candidates, having jeered from the sidelines for the best part of twenty years, are now faced with the terrifying prospect of actually forming a government.

Milltown folk may thump the table, after a few beers, and argue the political toss. But on the whole they subscribe to that old cliché: that whoever you vote for, it's the government that gets in. The drinkers who prop up the bar at the Grievous Bodily Arms have an even more cynical view, suggesting that our precious democracy is nothing more than three wolves and a lamb voting on what to have for lunch.

"Make mine a big one", says one of the regulars. "What do you think I am", replies the landlord, a disillusioned man with a face like a beef tomato, "a bleeding plastic surgeon?" . . .

3   Drinking to Forget

It is the sort of pub where they think shandy is a cocktail. Where a man with a full set of teeth is regarded as a tad effeminate. Where conversations usually start with "You can say what you like about Adolph Hitler, but . . .", and go swiftly downhill from there. Yes, it's the Grievous Bodily Arms: the naffest public house this side of the Crab Nebula.

The Town Drunk, though banned from many pubs in Milltown, is still welcome here - if 'welcome' is the right word to describe a pub with all the warmth and bonhomie of one of Woodie Allen's family reunions.

A collection of forensic photographs pinned to the wall represents one of the few attempts at decor. Behind the bar, gathering dust, is a small and worthless collection of trophies, recalling the pub regulars' achievements in darts, dominoes and formation ram-raiding. When the Grievous Bodily Arms won the After Midnight Car Door Slamming Contest three years in a row, they got to keep the trophy.

Town Drunk sits at the bar, staring blankly into the bottom of an empty beer glass and enjoying another evening of morose intro-spection: never a total waste of time. He drinks at the Grievous Bodily Arms whenever he feels life has dealt him a particularly unplayable hand. That's eight o'clock most nights.

The barmaid pulls him another pint of cooking bitter. He doesn't bother to look up; she has none of those feminine charms that might distract a hardened drinker. Imagine, if you will, Claire Short's less attractive sister, with rather more body hair than you'd expect from someone who isn't in the building trade. She divides her time between pulling pints and touting for casual abbatoir work. Some women sport a discreet little tattoo - a rose perhaps - but you'd imagine that having the words *Die, Bastards, Die* gouged artlessly into her forehead might be the source of a regretful twinge or two as the years slip by.

Monday night is quiz night at the Grievous Bodily Arms. The prize is generally a year's subscription to *Hard Bastard Monthly*, or a platter of raw meat: not so much a mixed grill as an autopsy. In deference to the pub's clientele, who are mostly from the shallow end of the gene pool, the questions are untaxing. Like: Who are you looking at? Wanna make something of it? Do you like hospital food?

Fortunately, Milltown has pubs to suit all tastes. The Flag, for example, caters for lovers of real ale, steam engines and computers: the sort of people who think there is something intrinsically funny about bad programming code. You can walk in, shout "anyone got a Maltese rail timetable handy?", and there'll be a stampede to offer you the requisite paperwork.

Beer is taken very seriously at the Flag. Beer Bore, on a crusade to find the perfect pint, is comparing his pint of Throgmorton's Old Throat Scourer with the last such pint he enjoyed. The pump-clip boasts that it is Brewed with Pennine Water - not particularly persuasive to people who know that the most palatable thing you are likely to find in a Pennine stream is a dead sheep.

He produces a little black notebook which details every pint he's ever drunk, with points out of ten for each one. Page after page of diminutive, obsessively neat handwriting: the sort of handwriting you see on Crimewatch, when Nick Ross quizzes the resident graphologist. "Are there any clues here that the writer would one day dress up in a clown costume, walk into MacDonalds with a pump-action rifle and blow twenty-seven people away?"

They certainly broke the mould when they made Beer Bore. They had to: some sort of health and safety regulation, apparently. He's at that difficult age when a man with a beard, two left feet, and time on his hands feels an irrational desire to take up Morris Dancing.

He buttonholes you with an enthusiasm that proves less than infectious, usually about beer, or steam trains or computers. "You'll find this interesting", he lies, as you suppress the urge to add: "Let me be the judge of that". If you were to suggest, unkindly, that he should get a life, Beer Bore will merely beam at you and say: "Now there's a coincidence; I'm busy downloading one" . . .

4   Passive Smugness

Unseasonably warm April weather is making Milltown bloom with flowers. The first swallows are here, recuperating after their long flight north. The trees, only half in leaf, are full of newly-arrived songbirds. The willow warbler's cadence evokes the summer days to come almost as vividly as the sighting of the first ice cream van. As he hurtles round another blind bend on two wheels, the ice cream man activates his chime. It is *Greensleeves,* played on what sounds like a Rolf Harris Stylophone and then blasted out at migraine-inducing volume to the blameless folk of Milltown.

And if the ice cream man is on his rounds, the first tourists can't be far behind. Milltown is quite a tourist honeypot these days, a fact which begs just one question. *Why?*

After all, we have none of those stately homes built by over-privileged aristocrats whose wealth derived from licking William the Conqueror's boots to most timely effect. Instead we have 'brass castles': the grand houses built by 19th century mill-owners. Not content with grinding the faces of the poor into the dirt, they built their ostentatious gritstone palaces on the hills above Milltown, just to aggravate even further the mill-workers cooped up in their unsanitary little Milltown hovels.

Some of these houses have been thoughtfully saved for the nation by the jack-booted custodians of the National Trust. The mill-workers 'paid' dearly - with their youth, their health and their lives - so that the mill-owners and their families could live in unbridled luxury. The descendents of these same mill-workers have to pay once again for a vicarious glimpse into this world of pampered privilege. So that's alright then...

From the vantage of his tiny office at the top of the town hall, our Tourism Officer gazes down over his domain: a dense pattern of tiled roofs, broken up by the saw-tooth profile of the old mills, and the few mill chimneys that still remain. It's his job to rewrite Milltown's chequered past, and persuade those with time on their hands and money in their pockets to spend them both in this unpretentious little Pennine town.

On sunny weekends the town fills up with tourists. Armed with brochures presenting a picture of Milltown that has all the soft-focus authenticity of a Hovis advert, they wander the streets looking for something to do. Since the closure of the Museum of Torture and Atrocities, we have few attractions that will keep fractious children amused for a couple of hours.

So what *do* we have? Well, there's the canal, a handful of tea-shops and a plethora of gift-shops. A strange concept, gifts. Things you give to other people that you really wouldn't thank them for giving to you. But visitors still need to acknowledge the momentous fact that they've been to Milltown. So thoughts turn, naturally enough, to souvenirs made in Taiwan and wonky hand-thrown pottery. Couldn't we encourage potters to cut out the middle-man and just toss their deformed offerings straight into a skip?

Milltown, being full of old hippies, has more than its fair share of vegetarians. For some reason it's never enough for vegetarians just to stop eating meat. No, they've got to be smug bastards as well. No problem finding where your veggie friends live: just look for the house with a visible aura of sanctity around it.

Some vegetarians think it's OK to eat fish. But has anyone polled the fish on this subject? Would you prefer a) to be caught by the gills, suffocate slowly and end up as a boil-in-the-bag Cod in Parsley Sauce meal for one, or b) swim around with your mates and die of old age?

Concerned carnivores who want to salve their consciences can buy 'conservation grade' meat. They will feel better, apparently, knowing that the animals they eat have enjoyed meaningful lives.

Each 'conservation grade' cut of meat carries a label, giving a brief history of the animal's life, pet-name (if any) and those endearing characteristics that had marked it out from the common herd. The 'conservation grade' charter promises that the animal will never have been spoken to in a gruff or threatening manner, and will have enjoyed at least three peak sexual experiences with the partner of its choice.

The end, when it came, is vouchsafed to have been both quick and painless: a lethal injection administered to the soothing strain of Mantovani strings. Deceased animals are given a short, non-denominational funeral service, before being sliced up into the bloodless, shrink-wrapped cuts neatly displayed on the supermarket shelves.

The expression 'the nearer the bone, the sweeter the meat' is put to the test as each carcass is then blasted with high-pressure hoses to recover every last bit of goodness: gristle, fat, cartilage, mucus and snot, as well as less savoury bodily fluids. These choice ingredients are ground to a fine slurry, mixed with belly-button fluff and formed into beefburger patties. So the thought occurs: what exactly goes into those *budget* burgers?

5   Rolling Up

S trangely, those who take pains to avoid eating meat aren't always so fastidious about the drugs they take. Some have been taking rather too many proscribed substances since the late sixties, which means that the height of their ambitions, thirty years on, is merely to keep track of their own saliva.

Dope Dealer is one such figure. As he sits in shadow, nursing a pint, his face seems to have imploded. He has the pallid complexion of the recently exhumed. It is almost reassuring to learn he is doing hard drugs; he could have looked that bad *all* the time.

He once had a frightening drug experience: he couldn't get hold of any. He had a lost weekend that lasted five years; now he's on extended leave from reality. The inside of his head, on a wet Monday morning, must be a lonely place to be. The last event he can recall with any clarity is a Bay City Rollers gig. Buying drugs off this guy would be like buying a used car from someone who had just caused a fifty-vehicle pile-up on the motorway.

Gone are those utopian dreams, those hopes for a better world. The big questions remain unanswered. Those of us who lived through the heady days of flower power are forced to admit, if pressed on the matter, that, no, we still don't know the way to San José.

Those whose IQs haven't yet slipped into single figures try at least to rationalise their drug habit - hoping that by taking drugs themselves, their children will rebel against them and not take any at all. It's a selfless attitude that typifies Milltown's responsible attitude to the demands of parenting. It will also explain, to social anthropologists of the future, why so many prominent public figures of the new millennium will be saddled with names such as Echo, Rainbow and Harmony.

The lucky ones, blessed with a modicum of self-control, confine their drug-taking activities to having the occasional shot of Night Nurse and then operating heavy machinery. One way or another the air above the town is so thick with hallucinogenic smoke that crows invading Milltown airspace are liable to drop out of the sky without warning.

Everyday life is chronicled in the local newspaper, the *Milltown Times:* a publication of few ambitions and even fewer readers. Even in a county of piss-poor parochial papers the *Milltown Times* manages to project an air of inertia and mediocrity. Old people read the paper merely to confirm that they haven't died in the night.

The pictures have a familiar look: hardly surprising since the gurning face of the town's mayor appears in nearly every one, presenting a huge cheque to the girl guide troop or chatting patronisingly to Milltown's oldest living resident.

There is always a selection of old photographs showing how Milltown looked when the mills were turning out fustian and corduroy, instead of being converted into cybercafés and artists' studios. People stand around in these pictures, gazing impassively at the photographer and giving the distinct impression that they have nothing more important to do. Very much like the Milltown of today, in fact.

Why try to parody the newspaper's headlines, when the real ones include: No Weather Records Broken, Milltown Man Creosotes Shed,

Bus Route Stays the Same and World War III Declared: No Milltown Residents Involved? (Oh alright, two are made up . . .)

6 Watching the River Sit

In some ways Milltown is a bit old-fashioned. It's the sort of place where an old guy can walk into the ironmongers and have realistic expectations of being able to find a new handle for his yard-broom. The pubs still look like pubs - even after a refit - rather than the flight-deck of Concorde or Barbara Cartland's boudoir. The fast food franchises (catering to the palate and attention span of a hyperactive six-year-old) have yet to blight our town with their vile offerings. And Snickers bars will always be Marathons to us.

We don't subscribe to the notion, so prevalent in the eighties, that living next to an industrial river is intrinsically more chic than living next to, say, a glue factory or knacker's yard. Milltown's own river is an unlovely and polluted watercourse, whose water is an impenetrable battleship grey. It offers no prospect of sophisticated waterfront living, nor even a tranquil riverside stroll. There are no paddlers on hot afternoons; no-one sane would even put a finger in.

The relics of the past are still very much with us. We may sand-blast smoke-blackened buildings back to their pre-industrial biscuit-brown facades. We may convert mills and warehouses into craft workshops and bijou residences. But the fabric of the town is essentially intact; evidence of our industrial history can be found wherever you look. In a society that seems to condone - even celebrate - the sham and the bogus, Milltown seems somehow authentic.

This is perhaps one reason why so many creative people have gravitated to the town - plus the fact that only twenty years ago you could buy one of the tiny 'top & bottom' houses for the petty cash you had in your back pocket. Prop up the bar of almost any pub in town (apart from the Grievous Bodily Arms, of course, where a tattoo of a pneumatic girl wrestling a python represents the height of artistic endeavour) and you'll be rubbing shoulders with writers, painters, conceptual artists, musicians

17

and commissioning editors from Channel 4.

We even have an arts festival when, for a few weeks each summer, empty mills are turned into galleries, the windows of Milltown's shops overflow with paintings, and venues large and small take the very necessary precaution of lowering the ceiling in an attempt to keep the jugglers out.

On any night during the festival you might see avant-guard dance collectives from Latvia, shy poets reading their verses from school exercise books or tone-deaf social workers singing unaccompanied sea shanties. The difficulty is not merely in deciding which performance to see, but whether to venture out at all if there happens to be a repeat of Pets Win Prizes on TV.

We are up to date in one respect, at least, with our very own presence on the Internet. The Milltown Web is a pioneering example of a whole community going on-line. Once they've set themselves up with the bare essentials - computer, modem, Internet service provider, appropriate software and the expectation of astronomical phone bills - the more computer-literate residents of Milltown can log on to the Internet and send emails to each other. Just think how much easier that is than walking a few yards and knocking on a door. We can now fax our orders to the Milltown pizza house; if it's a thin-crust pizza they can even fax it back.

The Internet attracts hysterical headlines about the availability of pornography - as though the top-shelf of Milltown's own newsagent wasn't a more convenient source of smut. And it's true that rather too many web-sites are just a waste of electrons: serving no useful purpose and proud of it. But pointing out that there are too many 'waste a bit more of your life' web-sites on the Internet is like complaining that a night of passion with Michelle Pfeiffer will make you lose sleep. True, but who cares?

Milltown isn't, of course, the only town that can boast its very own web-site. Smutty search engines ensure that the pages devoted to Penistone and Scunthorpe get a disproportionately large number of 'visitors' - even if most of them are likely to be disappointed at what they find when they get there.

Country Life

A shiny new Range Rover pulls into the little square in the middle of Milltown. It is the Smallholder family, venturing down from their luxury converted farmhouse in the hills, to patronise the locals and do a bit of shopping. Mr Smallholder parks where everyone will be able to admire his expensive new number plate. When you see someone whose car bears a personalised number plate, do you think: "You know, I really respect a man who, in a world of bland conformity, makes such a bold decision to stand out from the crowd"? Or do you just think: "Wanker . . ."?

Mr Smallholder does something mind-bogglingly pointless in Manchester's financial district and so, naturally enough, gets paid an absolute fortune. Complex and generous bonus schemes ensure that if he increases turnover, shuffles a lot of papers or merely manages to work an uninterrupted week, he will be rewarded with share options, golden handshakes and off-shore bank accounts. Now he and his family have swapped the crime and grime of the city for what they fondly imagine will be a rural idyll.

Blissfully unaware that proper farming represents a lifetime of mindless, back-breaking labour, working from dawn to dusk seven days a week (with maybe a couple of days off each year to attend Smithfield Show or a seminar about bulls' semen), Mrs Smallholder wants to get 'back to the land'. She has time on her hands and a rosy view of country life that stems from knowing nothing whatsoever about it.

A diet of glossy lifestyle magazines and shampoo adverts has given her unrealistic, soft-focus visions of wandering around her herb garden in a Laura Ashley frock, with a basket of meadow flowers hanging from her arm. She ordered what the salesman promised was a 'farmhouse kitchen' - all stripped pine and terracotta tiles - not realising that a genuine farmhouse kitchen is more likely to resemble a charnel house or motorbike mechanic's workshop.

On those rare occasions when the local farmers venture down below the tree-line, they need no persuading to air their jaundiced opinions on any subject you care to mention. But if you want to see a red-faced farmer positively incandescent with rage, you only have to drop the Smallholders' name casually into the conversation.

Mrs Smallholder wanders round the boutiques to enjoy a bit of retail therapy, but she's still unaccustomed to shopping in a small town. Her usual request - "Have you anything small, exquisitely useless and very, very expensive?" - cuts little ice here in Milltown.

Knowing it might take half an hour for her to reach her gold card limit, Mr Smallholder decides to investigate one of the pubs and have a pint. The Stoic, overlooking the town square, is a pub seemingly designed for people who want to avoid over-excitement. With its posh carpets, mindless musak and fancy-pants menu *(poisson, pommes frites avec pois mushy)* it is the sort of place you'd go to if you wanted to mollify a financially rapacious ex-wife. The pub tends to be patronised by men who carry purses, wear sheepskin driving coats and don't swear in mixed company . . . and their wives, who wear hats and drink sweet sherry.

This is the Sad Couple's local. They sit side by side, yoked together by mutual apathy, and stare blankly in opposite directions. They look like they last had a really good laugh about the time of the moon-landings. After years of joyless marriage the only thing they still have in common - apart from the right to be tried by jury - is the ability to make half a pint of bitter last a couple of hours.

They drive a battered Austin Allegro. If a bright-red Ferrari represents a tumescent erection in the common imagination, then the Austin Allegro presumably represents a painful prostate. The Sad Couple use it once a week to drive to some local beauty spot, sit with the windows closed and drink a flask of lukewarm tea.

Mr Smallholder waves his hand airily past the array of hand-pumps on the bar. "Now, then, landlord, what do you recommend?" "Two weeks in Barbados" comes the sour reply. At that moment Mr Smallholder is joined by his wife, laden down with bags, who squeals delightedly: "Just look what I found in this darling little shop . . . twigs. Fantastically expensive, I know, but I just *had* to have some".

8   Hold the Front Page

It's election day in Milltown and the inhabitants, reeling after six weeks of lies and braggadocio, are still wondering which bunch of hoodlums to vote for. The Town Drunk, for example, is weaving his way towards the polling station, ready to do his civic duty: spoiling his ballot paper with puerile invective and a yellow crayon.

Since there is nothing on the ballot paper to suggest that you can put your 'X' against 'Democracy', 'Fascist Junta', 'Banana Republic' or 'Enlightened Dictatorship', the only choice seems to be between one load of Identikit politicians and another. Or, for those who eschew politics altogether, there's always the Green Party.

The opinion polls suggest a Labour landslide. A lot of Milltown voters will think "It's a foregone conclusion; there's no need for me to vote" and risk letting the Tories back in again. It's a chilling notion, not least because most Tory MPs, having bowed to the inevitable, are already negotiating rewarding posts such as supplying anthrax spores to the Iraqis.

The pollsters and pundits managed to get it wrong in 1992, so Milltown folk won't take the result for granted until John Major climbs onto his soap box one last time and addresses the nation. "Remember all that guff about 'a classless society' and 'a nation at ease with itself'? Well, it was just a joke: we're *Conservatives,* for God's sake . . .".

"Here", says Beer Bore, well into his fifth lunchtime pint at the Flag, and prodding some hapless drinker's chest with a stubby forefinger, "How many Tory ministers does it take to change a light-bulb?" His victim shrugs his shoulders indifferently, so Beer Bore continues: "None . . . the official line is that not only is the bulb working fine it's actually getting brighter all the time".

Milltown folk wake up on a sunny morning - a 'new dawn' indeed - to find the political map has turned red in the night. The results exceed the expectations of even the most optimistic of Labour supporters. Who knows what finally clinched it: Labour policies, Tory sleaze or Andrew Lloyd-Webber's petulant promise to leave the country if Labour won?

Willow Woman went against her better instincts (which were to plump for the Natural Law Party and the obvious fiscal advantages of yogic flying) and voted Labour. The Tories had been in power for long enough, she decided. The last straw came when her grandmother had to go into hospital for a heart-swap operation. Unfortunately her heart was swapped for the transmission of a 1974 Ford Capri. Despite the hospital's crack team of fund-managers predicting a good outcome - "perhaps a small after-tax profit" - Willow Woman knew it was time for a change of government.

As we watch the TV pictures of Tony Blair posing outside Number 10, the feeling in Milltown is one of guarded optimism. Then again, we are the same gullible folk who imagine that pouring boiling water on a pot snack is going to transform a mixture of brick-dust and E-numbers into a tasty and nutritional meal.

The editor of the *Milltown Times* realises a lifetime's ambition by poking his head around the door of the editorial office (a broom cupboard equipped with a kettle and an ancient Remington typewriter) and yelling "Hold the front page" at his startled sub. The momentous events of the last twenty-four hours have not gone unnoticed here at the town's journalistic hotbed. "New headline", he barks, "Milltown Man Spoils Ballot Paper".

9   Wounded Man

The *Milltown Times* runs a regular column by the town's one celebrity export. He is a man whose huge affection for the town is indicated by the speed with which he decamped to London on being offered the important post of Deputy Head of Paperclips in Margaret Thatcher's government.

Now surplus to the requirements of any organisation with political leanings to the left of the Ku Klux Klan, he has been consigned to the rubber chicken circuit of minor celebrity. He feels obliged to offer his jaundiced opinions on every issue that affects the good people of Milltown, and labours under the misapprehension that we are as fascinated by his every word and gesture as he is himself.

In his achingly tedious role as a 'Professional Yorkshireman' he has rendered himself immune to the doubts and indecision that effect those lesser mortals who try to think before they talk. His is a simplistic world peopled with conspirators whose one aim is to stop our country becoming great again. He makes it his personal crusade to show them up for what they really are: namby-pamby, Guardian-reading lefties who look at both sides of every issue and then come down firmly on the fence.

Naturally, there are many blameless folk in Milltown for whom it is a badge of honour to have been on the receiving end of one of his regular tirades. And, since it's a sunny weekend, a lot of them are sitting around in the town's square. They pass the time by watching the world go by and discussing the options open to the terminally indolent: such six-pint topics as the relative merits of opening a flea circus or starting a cult religion.

There are quite a variety of street-styles on display. The crusties look as if they've been dipped into a vat of mud and then left to dry. Etiquette demands they have an equally unkempt dog on a bit of string and drink strong cider to the point of unconsciousness. Some have rings through ears, noses, lips and tongues. Rumour has it that one of them even has a pierced foreskin, though it turns out, on polite enquiry, to have been nothing more than an unfortunate industrial accident.

The hippies wear shapeless pantaloons and rainbow coloured sweaters. They too adopt an air of studied torpor, especially the older ones, who seem to have adopted - and then adapted - Timothy Leary's dictum to tune in, turn on and drop off. Willow Woman is chatting to some of her friends, including Wounded Man who, in a town full of men with straggly grey hair, is distinguished only by it not being worn in a ponytail. He has the sad rheumy eyes of an elderly Labrador, and nods understandingly as Willow Woman complains about the unwanted attention she gets from men . . . every time she walks into the super-market naked.

Wounded Man is a founder member of the Holistic Plumbers' Collective who, when called out, try to put plumbing problems into a more global context. Instead of just mending leaks or plumbing in washing machines they like to sit around at the customer's house, drinking coffee and consulting the *I Ching*. Only when they have fully explored their feelings do they make any effort to get down to work. By which point, in an unconscious homage to more conventional plumbing procedures, they usually find they've forgotten to bring their tools with them.

Stoical on such occasions, one of the collective will offer the well-meaning observation that "We obviously weren't meant to work today. Best put a bucket under that leak and call a proper plumber."

10   The Full Brontë

Milltown's Tourism Officer picks his way through the human debris in the square, like a fastidious rambler avoiding cow-pats. He's a worried man. His boss has just given him an ultimatum: "Get Milltown up there with Haworth and Holmfirth, pronto, or I'll shut down the Tourism Department and make sure you'll be filing paperwork all week".

Milltown isn't one of those 'look at me' villages, with picturesque thatched cottages or a village green fringed with spreading chestnut trees. And every successful tourism scam achieved by Milltown's neighbours is a dagger-thrust through our Tourism Officer's heart. "Anyway, what has Haworth got that Milltown hasn't?", he bleats piteously, to anyone in the Flag foolish enough to listen. "It's got the Brontës . . .", suggests Beer Bore. " . . . Yes, yes, yes, but what else?"

Well, it's got such a proliferation of cafés, craft-shops and tawdry Brontë souvenirs that any atmosphere this dour little town may once have had has been utterly obliterated. Milltown's Tourism Officer looks upon such popular attractions as the Branwell Brontë Massage Parlour and Tea-room with a mixture of envy and awe. Moved to investigate Milltown's own Brontë connections, he trawled the archives of the local history society. This attempt to climb aboard the Brontë gravy-train hit the buffers when weeks of diligent research revealed merely that Charlotte came to Milltown just the once, to have a boil lanced.

Holmfirth, to the south, has cashed in on the unfathomable success of *Last of the Summer Wine* - a success that makes our Tourism Officer almost weep with frustration. It's so unfair, since Milltown itself is overstocked with elderly buffoons who are locked into their second childhoods and have plenty of time on their hands.

As he strolls distractedly through the streets of Milltown, he recalls with a shudder some of his other doomed attempts to put Milltown on the tourism map. He had tried to attract film-makers to Milltown by stressing its gritty Northern authenticity. But the only film crew that ever came was making a video for a heavy-metal rock band.

Everyone in town was kitted out in period clothing for the occasion: dowdy frocks and bonnets for the women, moleskin trousers, waist-coats and flat caps for the men. Unfortunately the film crew ended up shooting the entire production in the slaughterhouse. Worse, the promised employment opportunities extended only to dwarves - plus a cameo role for Willow Woman as the Bride of Frankenstein. "The nude scene isn't just a gratuitous bit of tit and bum", the director lied convincingly, "it's an integral part of the plot, or something".

In an attempt to give the Milltown milieu a more distinctive identity, our Tourism Officer was encouraged by other high-profile initiatives. Sometimes all that's needed is a change of name. London's seedy Kings Cross area, for example, had been transformed into a tourist magnet simply by adopting the sobriquet of Jeffrey Archer Country. And what a reassurance it had been to environmentalists everywhere when Windscale Nuclear Power Station changed its name to Sellafield.

With the benefit of hindsight, however, Milltown's 'Welcome to Abbatoir Country' banners and lavish 'Offal World' brochures should never have got any further than the drawing board.

11   Amnesia Avenue

Local Writer sits at the bar of the Flag, leafing distractedly through a back issue of *Warm Beer Monthly*. As he removes yet another grey hair from the lapel of his shabby tweed jacket, he's feeling every one of his 46 years. He finds some little brown spots on the backs of his hands. Brown spots: isn't that what old guys have?

The ageing process starts almost imperceptibly, then picks up speed; Local Writer makes a mental note of a few tell-tale signs. At parties you don't try to chat up the available talent, you just hope you don't get stuck in a low chair. You tune into Radio 2 and find they're playing all your favourite songs. You listen to Richard Clayderman and you think: *"Aaaaawwwwllllriiighttt . . ."*.

Young people stop being 'us' and start being 'them'. Your conversations are peppered with meaningless refrains like "When I was your age . . .", "Of course, that was a lot of money in those days . . ." and "You know, maybe Mary Whitehouse wasn't taking bollocks after all". You are tempted by small-ads for sensible trousers in the tabloid papers, and when you go window shopping you find yourself gazing covetously at a Goblin Teasmade.

You develop an unaccountable interest in golf, gardening and church architecture. You have a strange desire to make a milky drink before bedtime and get a taste for shortbread biscuits. You think twice before buying a five-year diary. Worst of all, Tory policies start to make sense. It's disturbing.

All you've got to look forward to is losing memory capacity and control over vital sphincter muscles. And what then? Just a quiet stroll down Amnesia Avenue and an early grave. Local Writer ponders morosely what people would say about him when he'd gone: in an ideal world it would be "That bastard owed me money".

It's a bad case of writers' block that's brought on this rather depressing train of thought. Yet once it was all so very different. Even as a young lad he'd had a literary turn of mind: he was a page at his sister's wedding. And the writing career had begun so promisingly, with his first book winning the coveted *crouton d'or* at the Guernsey Book Fair. This inconsequential award emboldened him to resign from his safe but boring job - making wet-look trousers for the incontinent - to take the plunge and write full-time. The writer's life, he felt, had a lot to recommend it: the hours might have been poor but at least there was no heavy lifting.

He sold his house (which came as a bit of a surprise to his landlord) and moved to Milltown, the 'Hampstead of the North', hoping to rub shoulders with other bookish folk. However his first conversation with one of the town's other hacks was an inauspicious beginning. "I'm writing a book", he boasted. "That's a coincidence", came the reply, "neither am I . . .".

Local Writer's happiest inventions have been in the genre of the crime novel. It may seem strange that most of the private eyes in literature are antisocial, maladjusted loners. While this may not reflect the character of most private eyes, it's a serviceable description of your average writer.

12   The Feng Shui Man

Willow Woman gazes around her little terraced house in Milltown and she doesn't much like what she sees. Not even the accumulation of mobiles, crystals and wind-chimes can disguise the unpalatable fact that she is living in abject squalor. Having spent most of the winter trying to get on first-name terms with her inner child, she has managed to avoid such routine household chores as cleaning, washing up and emptying the cat litter tray.

The usual remedy - simply to light another joss stick - can no longer mask the malodorous atmosphere of grime and neglect. The clear rays of spring sunshine seem to permeate the gloomiest corners; even Willow Woman, generally unaware of the chaos in which she lives, realises that desperate remedies are called for. Springing immediately into action, she phones the Feng Shui Man.

Within minutes a fey young man is knocking on her door. Seemingly oblivious to the obvious health hazards he inspects each room in turn, nodding sagely and making notes. "I can tell you are a very spiritual person", he says. Having a pre-Galilean view of the cosmos - believing that all the planets revolve around *her* - Willow Woman nods appreciatively. "And you feel things more deeply than most people do." Willow Woman admits that, yes, this is indeed the case. "And not everybody understands, as I do, your need to go down the road less travelled". Willow Woman, impressed by the young man's insight, is now hanging on his every word.

View from the Bridge

"Are there any changes I can make", she asks him, deferentially, "that would help to create more harmony in my home?" The answer comes from her daughter, Sky, who clatters through the door in khaki fatigues and steel-toed boots: "You could always start by clearing up some of those cat turds, mum, they should be rock-hard by now".

Sky is counting the days until she can leave this pigsty for good. She thinks there's a very good reason why the road is less travelled: it's stultifying, a dead-end. The only road she's interested in travelling is the one that leads away from the stifling confines of Milltown.

She doesn't have much truck with new-age philosophies. The hippy-drippy 'All You Need is Love' stuff makes her want to go out and give someone a damn good kicking. After a childhood during which her mother could hardly decide what to cook for tea without consulting the I Ching, Sky has decided that actions do indeed speak louder than words.

The 1990s are throwing up some curious allegiances. Elderly ladies with blue-rinsed hair are manning the barricades alongside young activists like Sky and her friends. And Milltown is currently embroiled in a contentious issue of its own: plans for a hypermarket to be built on a patch of unprepossessing scrubland just outside of town. As soon as the plans were published, a makeshift army was mustered to thwart the developers at every step.

An environmental audit of the proposed site revealed a remarkable (though optimistic) variety of wildlife that would be lost to the bulldozers. Sightings of such rarities as the Natterjack Toad, Golden Eagle and Thompson's Gazelle underlined the value of the site to the local community. Until its transformation into a miniature Serengheti, the scrubland was mainly used by courting couples, dog-walkers and fly-tippers. Emboldened by rotgut cider the Town Drunk would spend balmy summer evenings there, exposing himself to passers-by.

Now there are alternative plans for this wasteland: a nature trail, picnic site and an interpretive centre. Environmental activists begin to move onto the site and construct tunnels and tree-houses. They are joined in their protest by more conventional Milltown folk, the eclectic nature of this raggle-taggle army emphasised by the placards being raised aloft: the messages range from 'Save Our Scrubland' to 'We Say NO to Casual Knitware' and - those Guardian readers - 'No Strong

Feelings Either Way'.

The editor of the *Milltown Times*, alert as ever to a good story, has dispatched his crack news photographer to the scene. She looks doubtfully at the hieroglyphics on her Kodak Instamatic - finally setting it to 'sunny' - and gazes myopically through the viewfinder at the diverse collection of demonstrators. "Smile" she says, absentmindedly.

13   Born to be Mild

Weaned from an early age on an unremitting diet of gangster films, Biker Dave left school at sixteen. "What's the point of education", he reasons, "when the villain always says 'We've got to kill you, 'cos you know too much'? Then, just to rub it in, he says 'Let the girl go, she doesn't know anything'."

It was bad luck to have found the only dyslexic tattooist in the area. All Dave wanted was to acknowledge his allegiance to those legendary outlaw bikers, Satan's Slaves. The tattooist was more than halfway through the job when he realised he'd bungled. His efforts to remedy the mistake, though well-intentioned, were ultimately misguided. Biker Dave was ushered smartly out of the tattoo parlour with the words 'Santa's Little Helper' inked indelibly into his fore-arm, alongside a charming portrayal of the Four House Martins of the Apocalypse.

This humiliation only made him redouble his efforts to embrace the life of an outlaw biker: an ambition that centred on doing drugs, shagging cool biker chicks and biting the heads off live chickens. But his first serious attempts at rebellion - taking two bottles into the shower, not rewinding rented videos and refusing, point blank, to use his postcode - soon stuttered to a halt. OK, it's not exactly the perfumed road to the eternal bonfire, but then this is Milltown, not Daytona Beach and, in any case, anarchy is relative.

Biker Dave lives on Hippy Street, a few doors down from Willow Woman and Sky, where you can expect, at any minute, to hear a knock on the door and a neighbour asking to borrow a cupful of money. The residents of Hippy Street take the idea of informal living to lengths undreamed of outside a Moroccan doss-house, and have a perverse pride in seeing just how much rubbish they can pile up outside their neglected properties. Willow Woman's one effort at gentrification - installing an outside bidet - failed to galvanise her neighbours into doing any home-improvements more taxing than hanging up yet another wind-chime.

Outside almost every house in Hippy Street is a vehicle of one sort or another - mostly in this year's fashionable two-tone colour scheme of rust and primer, with piles of house-bricks where the wheels ought to be. Geriatric VW vans bear mute witness to long-forgotten dreams of "really getting it together and going on the road", and the realisation, just minutes after purchase, that 'One Careful Owner' generally means 'One Careful Owner and Ten Homicidal Maniacs'.

In keeping with Hippy Street's relaxed attitude to interior decorating, Biker Dave's little house is an unprepossessing jumble of unwashed pots, bottles of rancid milk and semen-spattered underpants. A convincing idea of purgatory would be to have to walk barefoot over his bedroom carpet for eternity. Visitors tend to wipe their feet on the way *out*.

He once sweet-talked the barmaid from the Grievous Bodily Arms back to his house after closing time with offers of raw meat. She awoke next morning with a devastating hangover and a half-eaten cheese and tomato pizza spot-welded between her shoulder-blades.

Biker Dave's pride and joy is his motor-bike - an ancient Bastard 750 - which languishes in bits all over the house. With every effort to rebuilt it there seems to be more parts left over. It was after another unsuccessful attempt, and perhaps one pint too many, that Biker Dave took a sledgehammer to one of his partition walls. Encouraged by the result ("All that space", he thought) he decided to demolish the other interior walls too.

When the building inspector responded to a spate of anxious phone-calls from worried neighbours, he needed only the briefest glance inside. "Walk very, very slowly towards the door," he commanded in a hoarse whisper, "and don't make any sudden movements . . .", before slapping an unequivocal demolition order on what remained of Biker Dave's house.

14   The Biological Stains

It's Spring in Milltown and a young man's thoughts turn, naturally enough, to a lengthy session of colonic irrigation. There are many ways of responding to the sexual imperative. Town Drunk, for example, opts to stay home with a case of beer (24 cans in a case . . . 24 hours in a day . . . really just coincidence?) and watch re-runs of Baywatch with the sound turned down. As to the sex act itself, he's managed to get the whole unpleasant business down to about five minutes from start to finish. Even quicker in the implausible event that it's sex with another person.

Beer Bore, secure in the knowledge that no good ever comes from taking your trousers off, spends his quality time surfing the Internet in search of nude cartoon characters.

Wounded Man, feeling the need to be punished rather than cherished, is strangely attracted to dominant women: the kind who know that the quickest way to a man's heart is straight through the chest with a Stanley knife.

Whenever he's visiting this galaxy, Dope Dealer likes to invite a young lady round, and slip into something more comfortable . . . like unconsciousness.

Local Writer continues his lifelong search for a relationship more meaningful than that between a man and his newsagent. Brought up on rather more lyric poetry than is good for an impressionable young lad, he has long harboured unrealistic expectations of love and romance. Years ago, while his friends were splashing on that great smell of Brut and trying to score at the disco, he was taking long solitary walks in the countryside in the rather vain hope of surprising a young maiden bathing in the dappled sunlight of a woodland pool.

So it's no great surprise that now, after yet another lacklustre evening in the pub, Local Writer goes home to an empty house. He's just lucky that way. And what he decides to do in the privacy of his own home - with cheese-wire, a roll of cling-film, a punnet of soft fruit and perhaps some sort of primitive pulley system - is nobody's business but his.

View from the Bridge

Sky responds to Biker Dave's inept fumblings by kicking him in the balls: "Look", she says, with a finality that stems from wearing steel-capped boots, "there's no way I'll sleep with you . . . not even for a share of Fergie's air-miles."

Willow Woman talks a good deal about Tantric sex: the search for spiritual enlightenment through physical love. So it's one of life's little ironies that God made sex with a total stranger the most exciting sex you can ever have. At present (but it's still only Tuesday) she retains a soft, self-lubricating spot for a hairdresser who has staying power and a diploma in boring small talk. He prolongs his performance by recalling, ball by ball, one of Geoffrey Boycott's less rivetting innings. Just when he thinks the evening is heading nowhere, *he's* shot his load, *she's* faked an orgasm . . . and all's well with the world.

After a few pints the drinkers of Milltown develop an unaccountable craving for a kebab. They've completely forgotten about the last kebab they bought, the memories conveniently erased by a convivial evening of drinking beer and talking bollocks. They're so hungry they could eat a buttered handcart. So they wander hopefully into the take-away, where an grisly column of reconstituted meat has been heated up and then allowed to cool down every evening for about a fortnight, thus creating a sort of super-efficient stud-farm for salmonella bacteria.

"Make me one with everything" is their optimistic cry - echoing the spiritual aspirations of the Dalai Larma - as shavings of decomposing meat disappear into pitta bread, followed by limp salad and a chilli sauce whose main ingredient is battery acid.

When the punter is exactly a hundred yards from the take-away, he can't hold out any longer. He opens up his little parcel, takes a bite, and immediately realises he's been ripped off yet again. With the traditional cry of "I actually paid good money for this shit" he hurls the offending kebab over the hedge and into Wounded Man's tiny front garden.

15   Flannelled Fools

It's mid-May, the day of the Cup Final, so we can now look forward to a welcome break from footballing trivia. Cricket will enjoy an uninterrupted tenure of the newspapers' back pages for, oh, about six blissful weeks.

The members of the Milltown XI are career cricketers. At an age when county players are looking forward to the fruits of their second benefit year and ploughing the proceeds into a country pub or sports shop, we feel we are just coming to grips with the fundamentals of the game. This is why our opening bowler, a man of 46 summers, is still regarded as part of the team's youth policy. He probably has twenty more years of playing cricket in him. Then, since he has only the one good eye and a limited knowledge of the rules of cricket, he looks forward to donning the umpire's coat full-time.

The league umpires - small, dapper, pipe-smoking men well into their anecdotage - are kept in a shed during the week. Every Saturday the team captains come and take their pick, slipping the nominal umpiring fee into the breast pocket of an immaculately turned-out blazer.

There's not a lot to choose between one umpire and another. They all played cricket in their youth and, through the distorting lens of time, are convinced that the players of today aren't fit to lace the boots of the players *they* knew. If the umpires had a motto it would be: "The older I get, the better I was". Actually we are suspicious of 'stars': aggressive young lads who pace out long runs and expect to bowl throughout an innings. Or arrogant batsmen who hint that they are accustomed to a better class of cricket, and only want a few games with us to hone their technique before attempting to catch the selector's eye. We prefer a level of mediocrity to which even the least of our players can reasonably aspire.

We don't need stars because we don't really need to win. We *like* to win, and the beers afterwards taste a lot better if we do. But we don't *need to.* The pleasure derives not from the grand plan (there isn't one; strangely, we only talk tactics *after* the game), but from the inconsequential details that makes cricket so fascinating to those who love it, and so utterly unfathomable to those who don't.

The cricket ground is a reclaimed swamp, wedged between the malodorous river and the canal, backing onto the abbatoir. The natural habitat only of flannelled fools and malicious horseflies, the ground is so small that even the thinnest of snicks through the slips is liable to fly over the boundary for six.

With water so close at almost every point of the compass, such a shot is the cue for a young lad to leap, with practised ease, into a canoe conveniently tethered at the canal-bank. He paddles towards the ball, fishes it out, paddles back, ties up, gets out, hurls the ball arrow-straight into the wicket-keeper's gloves, and sits down again, as if this was an everyday occurrence. Which it is.

16   The Old Straight Track

Willow Woman operates a two-pronged strategy to avoid being burgled. She leaves her front door open, so burglars will think: "Nobody leaves their door open unless they're at home". Plan B - just in case this strategy fails - is to ensure her house looks so chaotic that any intruder who gains entry will assume she's already been burgled, and leave empty-handed.

Willow Woman's life is so painfully convoluted that Ken Russell considered making a film of it. Her response to everyday calamities is to bake. Using the smoke detector as a food timer, she turns out mountainous batches of inedible stoneground bread. It's called 'stoneground', incidentally, because its main constituent is gravel. Her loaves look like dead armadillos and Sky uses them for building barricades.

Despite the succession of men in her life, Willow Woman actually finds a relationship with two people in it rather overcrowded. You yearn to hear, just once, those magic words: "Well, that's enough about me;

what the hell is happening to *you?*"

Willow Woman is gorgeous - there's no doubt about it - and blessed with an award-winning bone structure. One of her most appreciative admirers is our Town Drunk; he has built up a small but select collection of underwear purloined from her washing line in Hippy Street.

In a way that would astonish the residents of, say, Cheltenham or Bath, the back-streets of Milltown are bedecked with washing lines. There are still women here whose perceived role as wife and mother demands that the family's clothes aren't merely clean, but seen to be clean. In the same way that shooting parties of the past would pose for a photograph with an obscenely huge pile of gamebirds, the women of Milltown like to put the fruits of their industry on public display. So it's a familiar noise, the crackle of sheets thrashing about in a drying wind.

In fact, the work ethic has been a cornerstone of Milltown life for generations, which is why the sight of work-shy young folk sitting around in the town square, downing alcopops and mulling over the big questions (like: have Waggon Wheels got smaller, or is it just that we've got bigger?) is anathema to the older generation. Yet the idlers make a colourful sight - like tropical birds tranquillised for transit to some far-off aviary.

It comes as a surprise to those untutored in the folklore of the 'old straight tracks' to discover that Milltown lies on the convergence of some very powerful ley-lines. It even surprises Willow Woman (usually happy to espouse any old mumbo-jumbo) when Wounded Man produces a scruffy map of Milltown, seemingly drawn by an artistically challenged five-year-old and criss-crossed with lines.

As a founder member of the Society for the Investigation of Unlikely Phenomena (Milltown Chapter), he has wasted many an evening searching for significances where none exist. "This line", he points out, stabbing the map at random with a grubby finger, "is in perfect alignment with three important landscape features: the church spire, this hollow tree and the public bar of the Grievous Bodily Arms". He leans back, feeling his point is proved beyond reasonable doubt, unaware that the back of Willow Woman's sofa is caked in fresh cat vomit.

But what *are* these lines? Ancient tracks? Landing strips for extra-terrestrial craft? Or merely the vapid outpourings of diseased minds?

Having researched the history of road protesting, Sky favours the first option. Indeed, she has unearthed exciting evidence that one of her distant ancestors tried - unsuccessfully - to thwart a controversial ley-line widening scheme.

17 Small Potatoes

It's a summer morning in Milltown and the shopkeepers are getting ready to open up. The Greengrocer sorts his deliveries, carefully putting the dirty, mis-shapen vegetables to one side. He stops his well-intentioned assistant from giving them a cosmetic scrub: "Don't do that", he admonishes, "just label them 'organic' and double the price".

Perhaps we shouldn't judge him too harshly. He's only trying to compete with the out-of-town supermarkets which he thinks are threatening his livelihood. The sort of places where you arrive at the checkout to find you've bought a bottle of chilli and oyster sauce, a packet of mange-tout, a sachet of Greek-style kebab marinade, a box of muesli, a tub of five-bean salad and a bottle of fizzy mineral water with just a *hint* of lime. You've forgotten to buy whatever it was you went in for, you've spent a week's wages, and you still haven't got anything you can actually *eat*.

Believing that 'if you can't beat 'em, join 'em', our Greengrocer has embarked on a steep learning curve. When sprouts weren't selling ("the kids just won't eat them", mothers would complain) it was a real brainwave to call them 'fairy cabbages'. He's going upmarket, attempting to titillate the palates of Milltown's more affluent shoppers with ever more exotic fare. Today it's a tray of rare fruit, flown in all the way from Kenya, which have all the appeal - and certainly the unappetising appearance - of an old man's scrotum.

Mrs Smallholder has already bought half a dozen, to enliven a small dinner party she is planning. The Greengrocer bites his lip, wishing all his customers were like her, instead of the daft old biddies who ask him for five pounds of spuds, and then tell him to pick small ones . . . "Because I've got to carry them home".

The shop next door is changing too. The Chemist has turned his back on years of supplying the good people of Milltown with essential - though unexciting - commodities, to relaunch his business as a pale imitation of the Body Shop. No longer can you find life's essentials, such as fungal cream, flavoured condoms or a box of suppositories. Instead he has adopted the sales philosophy of Anita Roddick. He acknowledges her saintly efforts to save the Third World from the horrors of dry skin, using the well-documented defoliant properties of Vimto and Branston Pickle. His pungent products aren't tested on animals, so God only knows what they're doing to us.

It's hard to imagine, as the rain bounces off the cobbled streets of Milltown, that the longest day is already behind us. We are now into the town's traditional holiday period - Glastonbury Week - when the inhabitants of Hippy Street decamp en masse to deepest Somerset. Even those who can't afford a ticket can still recreate the authentic Glastonbury experience right here in Milltown by not washing, setting light to a fistful of twenty pound notes, swallowing every pill in the medicine cabinet and spending three days of oblivion lying face down in litter and mud.

In any case, we are smack in the middle of our very own festival. Tonight there is a reading by what is billed as a 'well-known local poet': strange how the sobriquet 'well-known' is only ever applied to people you've never heard of. And an upstairs room at the Flag will be magically transformed into a folk club. This is the place to go if you want to join a compact gathering of the saddest-looking people you've ever seen.

"Hi, I'm Kevin", says Kevin, "I'd like to start the evening off with a song about whaling". He runs the Flag Folk Club only because he'd never get a singing spot, on merit, at any other club. When he fluffs verse 12 of his 15-verse ballad, his attempt to start again from the very beginning is drowned out by a desperate rush to the bar.

18   Coming to Grief

It is generally agreed that the Milltown take-away's 'Sign Our Condolence Book and Win a Kebab' promotion has hit exactly the right tone of reverence and commercial opportunism during these difficult times. What no-one could have foreseen was that, in lieu of a more appropriate site, these undistinguished premises should have become the focus for the town's grief: a veritable shrine to Diana, Princess of Hearts. Hungry customers can hardly squeeze through the door for the bunches of flowers, cards, mawkish poems and teddy bears piled high on the pavement outside: heartfelt tributes which workmen are already transferring - with all the sensitivity and solemnity the occasion demands - into a council rubbish skip.

It's an easy mistake to make: confusing someone you've only *ever* seen on the cover of glossy magazines for someone you actually *know*. But this is not a mistake made by the regulars of the Grievous Bodily Arms, whose sour and sullen opinions about a life cut so cruelly short are mostly unprintable. Not because of the sentiments expressed but because, after a few pints, these career drinkers have lost the ability altogether to articulate recognisable words. Nevertheless, with the help of a grotesquely extended Happy Hour (April to October) they are doing their very best to return to what passes for normality here in Milltown.

Elsewhere, ensconced at the bar of the Flag, Local Writer is busy losing some memory capacity and pondering an uncertain literary future. Where else but in Milltown, he wonders to himself, could a humble scribe be woken up at three o'clock in the morning by an agitated phone call: "Help, I need 2,000 words on angst and mortality, and I need them *yesterday*".

He sits alone. Wasn't it was Jean Paul Sartre who said "Hell is other people"? All his friends were French, so he must have known what he was talking about.

A publisher has just returned, in a plain brown wrapper, Local Writer's proposal for a book - *The Satanic Pulses: a Vegetarian*

Cookbook - that would attempt to capitalise on the worldwide success of Salman Rushdie's seminal work. The rejection slip, formed from words snipped out of tabloid newspapers, intimated that the publishing house had gone ex-directory, and pleaded with him, in a surprisingly plaintive tone, never to contact them ever again.

It was a strange sort of post altogether. From his breast pocket Local Writer produces a letter from his bank which proves to be an intriguing exception to the usual computer-generated threats to end his overdraft facility. He reads it to himself in wonderment . . .

> *Dear Local Writer,*
> *We are writing to offer our warmest congratulations that your account, unusually, seems to be in credit. On behalf of all our counter staff and tellers, may I just say 'well done',*
>
> *Yours sincerely*
> *Your Bank Manager*

Equally amazing was how it got delivered at all, since the envelope was addressed to "Local Writer, c/o Fantasy Island".

19   Answering the Call

Autumn has arrived in Milltown. Having delivered his usual post-mortem on yet another lacklustre season of predictable under-achievement, our cricket captain offers his resignation - as he has done every October for the last twenty years. He's tired, disillusioned and nauseated by the smell of horse liniment. As he hurls his unwashed kit into the back of the wardrobe, he insists he's played his last game.

But winter will wipe away the feelings of failure that smart so much today. Next spring he will have a change of heart, think "maybe just one more season" and discover that the indelible grass stains on his flannels have been supplemented by a bad case of mildew. And, unaccountably, the waistband of his trousers will have shrunk about an inch.

As the evenings get shorter, the locals have a depressing foretaste of the long Pennine winter to come. Wounded Man feels the seasonal changes more than most. Indeed, it was largely to assuage his own feelings of futility and despair that he decided to join the Milltown branch of the Samaritans. He hoped that listening to other peoples' misery might help to cheer him up.

It wasn't long before he saw ways to bring the organisation more up-to date. Why, he wondered, should listening to callers' problems preclude spinning a little profit? He supplied his own answer by brokering a ground-breaking sponsorship deal with the Milltown Kebab Take-Away. It had to be shelved, though, when volunteers were instructed to substitute their opening question, "Can I help you?", for the more familiar fast-food mantra, "Is that to eat in or take out?".

While no-one doubted his sincerity, there were some who questioned Wounded Man's methods. His enthusiasm for change extended to the setting up of an automated answering service. Callers would hear a well-modulated female voice enjoining those with a touch-tone phone to "Press 1 if you feel suicidal, press 2 if you want to have a wank, press 3 if you just want to waste our time". However, putting non-urgent callers on hold and forcing them to listen to a tinny rendition of the Last Post was reckoned to fall below the Samaritans' high standards of empathy and understanding.

What finally brought his career as a Samaritan to a premature halt was his suggestion for a uniform that would give the Samaritans a recognisable identity and help put despairing visitors at their ease. But when he turned up at the centre one day, wearing a full-face leather mask, with eye-holes, zips down the side and the word 'Samaritan' picked out in brass studs on the forehead, his fellow volunteers showed him the door with a collective and heartfelt sigh of relief.

20 Rallying Round

It's Saturday in Milltown and, it must be said, everywhere else as well. We've just had a vintage car rally. A desultory crowd gathered to watch the vehicles as they passed by; strange, really, since a parade of noisy, smoky, clapped-out old bangers is a regular spectacle in Milltown. Considering the global impact of the internal combustion engine, you might as well have a weekend celebration of, say, nerve gas or Agent Orange.

The sluggish parade held up the progress of Mr Smallholder's Range Rover for a few precious seconds, reducing him to impotent rage. Sitting at the crossroads, with knuckles white on the steering wheel, he tried, in vain, to rationalise the situation. "What if I drive straight through this parade: what's the worst that can happen? OK, I'll kill a few people . . . But I'll get to the golf match on time, kow-tow to a few influential clients, clinch the deal and earn pots of money . . .". For a lifelong Tory voter these are by no means rhetorical questions.

His murderous reverie is interrupted by the insistent ringing of his mobile phone. It is Mrs Smallholder, reminding him to drop the car off at Lesbian Motors of Milltown, for their heavily advertised executive valeting service. "And make sure they do a proper job", she reminds him. "All they did last time was check the oil, empty the ashtrays and change the suckers on the Garfield".

When Princess Diana was killed, the landlord of the Grievous Bodily Arms lost a great role model: yes, the driver, whose cheerful willingness to drive while totally pissed will be remembered long after it has been forgotten. "I actually drive better when I've had a few", says the landlord, with the misplaced confidence of the damned.

He has only managed to hang onto his licence because whenever he causes a spectacular pile-up around town, the Milltown police blithely assume it's just another exhibition of performance art. His ability to get from 0-60mph in the pub's car-park impresses those of his customers who are a long way down the food chain. And in deference to his unrivalled skill in leaving the scene of the crime at speed, he has been rewarded by a grateful local mafia with a *company* getaway car.

21   Pick 'n Mix Religion

Now that religion has largely been supplanted in the national psyche by visits to garden centres and car boot sales, a lot of people are finding there's a big hole in their lives where blind, unquestioning faith used to be. After all, how much spiritual comfort can be drawn from haggling over the price of a pot-plant or a second-hand Hoover?

The new vicar of Milltown knows the problem only too well. His church - an unprepossessing, smoke-blackened pile - echoes emptily every Sunday morning with the thin, reedy voices of his elderly parishioners. It was during Queen Victoria's reign (long before hellfire and damnation had been relegated to the status of mere lifestyle options) that the decision was taken to demolish the quaint little medieval church and erect a building more in keeping with Milltown's civic aspirations. No sooner had the new church been consecrated than the congregations went into a decline that's continued ever since.

As a man who's never yet seen a bandwagon he didn't like, our vicar is ready for the challenge ahead. Hoping to attract a few of those lost souls who can't tell the difference between religion and brand loyalty, he has bowed to the fickle outpourings of public sentiment. He's taken down the placards in front of the church featuring those excruciating puns dreamed up at central office, and replaced them with an imposing new sign. He allows himself a few moments of indulgence to admire his handiwork - 'Welcome to the Church of Diana', it says, in dignified day-glo lettering - before scurrying back into the the church to replace the hymn-sheets with copies of the *Elton John Songbook*.

Of course, there are many people in Milltown who would no sooner go to church that wear jam in their hair. People who dismiss Biblical miracles as being unfeasible, yet manage to weld together such disparate notions as UFOs, Feng Shui and past-life regression into a pick 'n mix portfolio of irrationality. Some of them are so relaxed, after years of therapy and meditation, that they are no longer able to stand upright unaided. So relaxed, indeed, that they take Valium as a stimulant.   Wounded Man, for example, has found his own spiritual niche, consisting mostly of hugging women and talking bollocks: a role for which he is eminently suited. He's got the half-witted look of a man who has been closetted in a small room with a large pile of dry-cleaning. It's an expression that a remarkable number of women mistake for spiritual profundity. To supplement his meagre wages as a Cyberpet Premature Demise Trauma Counsellor, he has carved out a small career offering oven-ready platitudes to his undemanding devotees: the sort of people still unsure whether shiatsu is an alternative therapy or a type of long-haired cat.

Years of training have given Wounded Man a number of skills vital to his role as a counsellor: the ability to listen, to empathise uncritically and - most important of all - to yawn with his mouth closed.

22   Talk of the Devil

It's Halloween Night. The children of Milltown - dressed up as witches and wizards - are demanding money with menaces from unsuspecting householders. The vicar looks on in frustration, wishing there was a way *he* could incorporate devil-worship into the church's calendar of sacraments, without alienating the more traditional members of his congregation.

The landlord of the Grievous Bodily Arms is boiling up a cauldron of oil in case any 'trick or treaters' have the temerity to call. This is not one of those pubs where businessmen go for lunch, with their braying voices, over-loud laughter and mobile phones. It's where strange, violent men with eyebrows that meet in the middle go to plan bank heists. While pubs such as the Flag feature guest beers, the Grievous Bodily Arms has guest *bouncers*.

What Milltown lacks, according to the drinkers propping up the bar, is a reputable brothel and an all-night pawnbroker. While you'd be unwise to ask for credit here, the barmaid can be quite obliging if a regular customer tips her the wink and rustles a fiver meaningfully between finger and thumb. So she makes a little money on the side by taking regular punters home after closing-time. She specialises in the things that women won't let their husbands do - like putting their elbows on the table and cutting their toenails in bed.

Best not try to catch the barmaid's eye over at the Stoic for anything other than a glass of lukewarm beer. An expectant cry of "A loose woman, please, and a side-order of floosies" is likely to fall on deaf ears here at this most genteel of pubs. The landlord prides himself on keeping an orderly house. For example, he only stocks ready-salted crisps, fearing that more exotic flavours might over-excite his customers.

The Stoic boasts a cosmopolitan menu. There's Aylesbury Duck, York Ham, Wensleydale Cheese and - the speciality of the house - Steak Canadian, made of tasty left-overs from the tanning industry. The landlord has decided, with no logic whatsoever, that tonight is 'Hawaiian Night' at the Stoic: an occasion that merely demands that chef opens up an extra can of pineapple chunks. Chef's ability to twist a thin slice of cucumber through ninety degrees has made his garnishes the stuff of legend. By excluding skill and discretion from the cooking process, and abandoning cuisine for portion control, he has ensured that the Stoic sets the standard by which other pubs' food is judged.

Town Drunk is on his best behaviour. Having lined his stomach with cleaning fluids, he is enjoying a small aperitif at the Stoic, prior to returning home for that rarest of treats: a home-cooked meal. Attempts to follow a more balanced diet have led him to choose a different pizza topping every day of the week. On the menu tonight is the contents of a full grill-pan - warmed up, spread thickly on toast and accompanied by a colourful selection of cheese stalactites, harvested from the racks in his oven.

23   The Numbers Game

O f all the ways to find long-lost members of your family, none is more effective than winning the National Lottery. This is not, however, a problem that needs to be addressed tonight by disgruntled Milltown punters. It's a depressing thought, as they rip up their tickets, that they'll have to keep their old friends and family for yet another week.

It's one of life's quaint anomalies that those who claim paranormal powers seem quite unable to pick the lottery numbers. When Uri Geller, for example, arrives at the pearly gates, and St Peter asks him to justify himself, all he'll have to offer will be: "I bent cutlery and nobody found out how I did it". Willow Woman, the loveliest of Milltown's many charlatans, is another whose powers fall inconveniently short. She can offer bland reassurances and the vaguest of prophecies, based on the turn of a Tarot card, yet cannot predict anything genuinely useful - such as those six numbers and the bonus ball.

It's Saturday night so the Sad Couple have taken up their customary seats at the Stoic, and stare fixedly at the point where the wall meets the ceiling. She turns unexpectedly to he: "What would you do if you won the lottery?"; he turns to she: "I'd send you a postcard".

Biker Dave is another lottery loser. He chooses exactly the same numbers every week: based on IQ, penis length and the number-plate of his Bastard 750 motor-bike. This simplifies matters by keeps the numbers in single figures, which is good. But using the same numbers every week locks him into the lottery habit, which is bad. If he were ever to miss a week, and 'his' numbers came up, he'd probably top himself.

If he was a bit brighter he would see the folly of his ways. If he was a bit brighter still, he would stop doing the lottery altogether. As our Town Drunk pronounces, in one of his rare moment of clarity: "I may spend all my money on beer and fags, but at least it's better than just frittering it away".

It's all rather different for the directors of Camelot. They may join the rest of the population in picking six numbers at random. But then they write them on a cheque, with their name at the top, and bank it.

24 The Ego Has Landed

It's Sunday morning in Milltown, and Councillor Prattle turns on the radio. Kate Adie is filing her report from the Gulf: a sure sign that conflict cannot be far away. Conflict makes Councillor Prattle's heart beat faster; for those who give their time to local politics - freely and without thought of personal gain - it acts like an intravenous shot of testosterone.

Councillor Prattle is not the kind of man to hide his light under a bushel. Where would you find a bushel large enough? Blessed with the sallow complexion of a seventies porn star, he has a face the colour and consistency of glazier's putty. And beneath that unprepossessing exterior beats a heart of stone. Although he claims to represent the electorate, all he actually represents is *himself*.

For a little fish in a little pond, his self-belief is Napoleonic. Nevertheless, you could fit his talent into a small box of matches - without taking out the matches. The thought occurs: instead of pissing in the cesspool of local politics, wouldn't he be happier closeted in his bedroom, armed with a full-length mirror and a bottle of baby oil?

He has certainly perfected the art of photo-friendly posturing, and his ferocious smile leers out every week from the pages of the *Milltown Times*. He writes long, self-justifying letters to the paper about issues which engage the obsessive attentions of rival councillors - but nobody else. Heavy on insult, and written in orange crayon, his rabid outpourings successfully keep common sense at arms length. The effect of this prolonged correspondence resembles nothing so much as a pack of polecats fighting over the mastery of a septic tank.

The latest issue of the *Milltown Times* contains an article about how Christmas seems to begin earlier and earlier each year. Isn't it strange how this kind of article seems to appear earlier and earlier each year?

The shops have cleared out their stocks of tatty Halloween junk (memo to the manager of Milltown's supermarket: don't *ready-made* pumpkin lanterns rather miss the point?). The shelves are now full of tatty Christmas junk which will be on sale for half-price by Boxing Day.

Postcards appear in the newsagent's window, written by opportunistic folk with stuff to sell. Artificial leg: ideal Christmas present . . . Two tons of dressed Yorkshire paving stones: ideal Christmas present . . . Yet who can deny the first stirrings of those festive feelings: an almost palpable air of avarice, sloth, greed and envy.

25   Stairlift to Heaven

Y ou can find live music most nights of the week in Milltown. There's the folk club in the upstairs room at the Flag, of course, where adenoidal nurses from Cleckheaton routinely murder ancient songs of lust and revenge. But it's not every band that would automatically pencil Milltown into their tour itinerary. So those bands which do play here tend to fall into one of three categories: those trying to climb *up* the greasy pole of pop celebrity, those sliding inexorably *down,* and those - like The Uncles - who, after years of stolid endeavour, are going precisely nowhere.

It's way too late for these Milltown-based soft-rockers to attract more fans than can be fitted into the back room of a pub. And on those increasingly rare occasions when an ardent fan tosses her underwear onto the stage, it's most likely to be a pair of incontinence pants. Four old guys with paunches and straggly pony-tails, strumming their way through yet another rendition of 'Stairlift to Heaven' . . . what could you possibly say about them that hasn't already been said about Formica? It must have been a very quiet news week when, a few years ago, the *NME* allotted The Uncles half a column of flattering newsprint, and dubbed them the 'Hardest Working Band in the Country'. This back-handed compliment emphasised that despite playing almost every night of the week in some dreary northern town they have conspicuously failed to attract the slightest glimmer of interest from a record company.

They're still on the road (they hardly dare stop, in case they seize up), but the years have mellowed The Uncles. Their days of hell-raising are over. Persistent (and short-sighted) groupies who manage to sneak into the band's dressing room will probably be asked to make up a foursome at bridge. Instead of trashing hotel rooms the band members prefer to tidy up and do a little light dusting. After a gig they look forward to cradling a mug of Horlicks and having an early night. They are back in Milltown this week, on the last leg of their 'Still Alive' tour. And even their most ardent fan (Wounded Man, since you ask) prays it will be their last.

26   A Hint of Heresy

The Stoic is a haven for beleaguered monarchists. It's the sort of pub where people say "What would we do without the Royal Family?", and expect to have their unswerving devotion reflected back at them. "Yes, aren't they marvellous" is the correct response if you want to avoid an argument. Don't bother suggesting that we might just as well replace the entire Royal Family by a troupe of over-sexed chimpanzees.

The regulars raise their glasses today to the royal couple who are celebrating their Golden Anniversary. Instead of spending the occasion lounging around at Balmoral, eating shortbread biscuits or sportingly blasting semi-domesticated game-birds out of the sky, the Queen and Prince Philip are out meeting their loyal subjects. "And what do you do, peasant?", inquires the Queen, trying in vain to suppress a yawn. "I work a backbreaking 10-hour shift, ma'am, for the sort of money that you probably shell out for a half-decent bottle of port", replies a man at the front of the crowd, before being felled by a barrage of police truncheons.

The Royal Family brings in millions of tourists, the loyal subjects in the Stoic are quick to point out. No problem: we'll lay on other diversions to keep the crowds amused. We could hold public floggings, to make examples of persistent offenders, like shoplifters, single parents and eaters of biscuits in bed.

If, as some suggest, the royal yacht Britannia has been such a big earner of foreign currency, then why the hell are we scrapping it? Why aren't we building a whole fleet of royal yachts and making some serious money? At least Windsor Castle has been lovingly restored to the way it was before the fire. You have to sympathise: it's no fun when one of your holiday homes burns down.

We all need someone to look up to, insist the Stoic's regulars. And that may be true. It's just bizarre that we should direct our deference towards a bunch of unelected parasites who think that every street is red-carpeted and that everything smells of paint . . .

27 Catching the Post

Time seems to be standing still in Milltown. We've recovered from the almost unbearable excitement of bonfire night, and now there's nothing much to look forward to until next spring. The sub-editor on the *Milltown Times* has used up his allocation of 'mist and mellow fruitfulness' banalities, and doesn't want to waste the Christmas clichés before what we laughingly call the festive season has really got underway.

Mrs Smallholder, too, is wrestling with the intricacies of the English language. She hammers away one-fingered on her laptop computer, like a demented woodpecker, to complete the now-traditional task of putting together a couple of circular, end-of-year letters. She has to go through her address book with a highlighter pen and a bottle of Tippex, to decide who gets which.

Dear friends,

It's Christmas time again, when the Smallholder clan gathers together in the family home: to carve the traditional roast leg of vegan, uncork a bottle or two of the finest Moroccan Rioja and raise a glass to all the dreadful people we've managed to avoid for yet another year.

You will, of course, be keen to know how the Smallholder family has fared during 1997. The simple truth is that we are very busy, very successful, and very, very smug.

The past year has been both exciting and challenging. The financial sector continues to prosper, allowing us to offer gainful employment to a number of Phillipino housemaids who are, thankfully, already accustomed to a brutal regime of poorly-paid manual labour.

The compliments of the season from the Smallholder Family

The other circular is proving more onerous. Mrs Smallholder has to call upon her vast reserves of tact and diplomacy when writing to those whose very existence comprises a negative lifestyle statement.

Dear ex-friends,

Just a quick note, as we approach the festive season, to inform you that you no longer dovetail into our portfolio of friends and acquaintances. We thank you for your friendship in past years, and trust that you will understand our unenviable predicament. Please delete our address, phone number and web-site from your own database, and never ever contact us again. Yes, really.

The compliments of the season from the Smallholder family

28   Open-collar workers

A lot of Milltown folk work from home. Very convenient for writers and designers, of course, but a bit of a bugger for deep-sea divers. To the notion of 'blue collar workers' and 'white collar workers', we have added another category: 'open collar workers', who believe, reasonably enough, that ties restrict the supply of oxygen to the brain.

It's a term that might suggest a life of indolence and unruffled ease:

sprawled on a sofa, eating continental chocolates and watching daytime TV. This is certainly true of our Town Drunk, the Jersey Royal of couch potatoes and a long-term signatory to one of the government's lesser-known Work Avoidance Schemes. He manages to fritter away the long hours while the pubs are shut by wrapping himself in a soiled duvet and checking out what's happening in Tellytubby land. Given his limited horizons and garbled speech it's a place where he feels very much at home.

However, for most of those who work from home the everyday reality is more likely to be penury, self-doubt and social isolation. It's a problem that is routinely addressed by the alternative practitioners and healers who have gravitated to the town. On a wet November day there are dozens of unfulfilled folk waiting in small ante-rooms all over Milltown: people who could benefit from some gentle counselling. Unfortunately most of them are therapists.

So who are these therapists, these artful purveyors of hokum to the hopeless? Most of them claim to be qualified, though not necessarily in the disciplines they practise. And the clientele? Mostly troubled folk who, having lost faith in conventional medicine, happily entrust themselves to self-appointed therapists. After all, how can seven years hard slog at medical college compare with a GCSE in corn-dolly making and a collection of *Readers Digest* articles about faith healing?

Since anyone can set themselves up as a therapist, it's no surprise that there are rented rooms all over Milltown manned by obliging charlatans. You might want to take a good long look at some of these unregulated teapots before entrusting them with your mental equilibrium. After all, would you hire the services of a fingerless carpenter?

29   Celluloid Heroes

Milltown's municipal cinema dates back to 1928. The casual visitor might wonder why it was built in the incongruous shape of an Egyptian mausoleum. Was it inspired by the first, silent version of Cleopatra? Or was it just the result of a mix-up between a junior architect and an overworked member of the town planning department, due to a crackly phone line?

We're always a little late in getting the blockbuster films: those big, dumb, action movies aimed at folk blessed with the attention span of a particularly inattentive goldfish. This week, for example, it's classic high-octane hokum - True Hard Double Mortal Instinct Target - featuring a bunch of American actors in sweaty singlets trying to outrun fireballs. You'll find more violence in ninety minutes of overwrought drama than you'd see in the Grievous Bodily Arms over an entire bank holiday weekend.

Mostly we like more stimulating cinematic fare. We can cope with foreign films, sub-titles, cult classics . . . even some old-fashioned wartime tosh featuring a troupe of crack English character actors being parachuted in behind enemy lines. And Milltown is the one place where a trailer for *The first film by a young Canadian director about the love between two women* makes us check our diaries in the hope of finding a free evening.

A Boy, a Girl and a Donkey is a perennial favourite. Filmed around Milltown - in grainy black & white with a budget of 49/6d - it's a stark tale of unrequited love and social upheaval set in a smoke-blackened Northern town.

A controversial hint of bestiality ensured that the vital third reel of the only surviving copy disappeared into the archives of a specialist collector. However, the undemanding viewers don't seem to notice the slight lack of continuity. One minute the heroine is spurning the gauche advances of the leading man, and his offer to set her up in a back-to-back hovel sandwiched between the abbatoir and the glue factory. Then, without warning or explanation, she is ensconced in the Big

House on the Hill with a donkey called Gerald.

Though the use of Northern stereotypes has seldom been bettered, these days the film's appeal is nine-tenths nostalgia. When the foreman calls at the Big House, tugging his forelock and wringing his cloth-clap, to announce that there's "trouble at 't mill", Milltown audiences cheer and throw popcorn. When the hero disconsolately finds that the whippets have eaten all his pigeons, there's hardly a dry seat in the house.

We enjoy watching the discomfiture of plummy southern actors trying to come to terms with the 'Learn Yorkshire Dialect in a Week' school of film-making. And Milltown folk have enthusiastically taken up some of the more ludicrous dialogue, dreamed up by a writer who obviously didn't have enough irony in his diet. "Ay lad", you'll hear the locals insist, "we may 'ave been poor, but by God we were picturesque".

30   A Dying Art

Now that the looms of Milltown have stopped clattering, what have we done with all those redundant mills? Well, some have been converted into upmarket homes. Some house more viable businesses. Some, unloved and unwanted, have been allowed to fall down. And one or two have found temporary uses as artists' studios.

What our talentless daubers get for their peppercorn rents is a little haven in which to flesh out their artistic fantasies. Or at least somewhere to escape from the kids and enjoy a few untroubled hours reading back issues of *Big & Bouncy*. Wounded Man, for example, has his own sanctuary: a cold and draughty loft with a birds'-eye view overlooking the tiled roofs of Milltown. Here his tepid imagination can take flight.

He gets even more misty-eyed than usual when he thinks back to the sixties. Those were the days, he recalls, when you could tell an artist by the paint spattered on his smock, instead of the all-pervading smell of formaldehyde and embalming fluid. He thinks back to the time he spent at art college: creating huge environmental sculptures with a hired JCB, finishing off the fine detail with a lump hammer. These early experiences gave him a good grounding in the conceptual art he practices today.

Proud to be putting the 'con' back into conceptual art, Wounded Man spends a lot of time these days just thinking about making things. Sometimes he just exhibits his notepads. Sometimes he just *thinks* about exhibiting his notepads. This uncompromising attitude puts him in the vanguard of Milltown artists, for whom indolence can be regarded as a mission statement.

The Milltown Gallery, occupying the ground floor of the same mill, exhibits the work of many local artists, including Wounded Man's blank canvasses and empty frames. It gets full, but only once a month, when the glitterati flock to the first night of each new exhibition. They stand around, quaffing cheap white wine and munching something greasy on a Ritz cracker, happy to part with folding money for a galvanised bucket in a gallery. P T Barnum would have recognised them with gleeful antic- ipation.

Mr Smallholder is one of Milltown's most dedicated art collectors. Careful not to let sentiment get in the way of a good investment, he keeps original artworks locked away in a bank vault and proudly displays the certificates of authenticity instead.

31 School Days

It's frosty in Milltown, on the morning that the government launches its Christmas crackdown on drink-drivers. It's a headache for the landlord of the Grievous Bodily Arms who thinks, sensibly enough, that if there's even the slightest chance of him being catapulted through the car windscreen, then he'd prefer not to be stone cold sober when it happens.

Parents are walking their children to school, before going off to work or back home to do the chores. But it's different for those parents who send their school to the Spooner School. They take their kids to school each morning . . . and then stay there.

In summer the parents sit on the school lawn; with their colourful pantaloons, imaginative hairstyles and animated chatter they seem like a flock of tropical birds. Now, at the onset of winter, the Spooner School parents prefer the cosiness of the drying room. While their children are in class, training to be corn-dolly makers, they warm their backs on the central heating pipes and mull over the big questions. Like: whatever happened to the Bermuda Triangle? In the 1970s ships and planes were vanishing on a daily basis. And now it's disappeared. Without warning. Weird.

The school's reputation extends far beyond these valleys. People raise their eyebrows, tap their nose with a knowing forefinger and say "Oh yes, the Spooner School". In the same mildly exasperated tone of voice that you'd say "Oh yes, California", on hearing about some loon getting his goldfish psychoanalysed.

Parents gravitate from all over the country to send their children to the Spooner School in Milltown. Having conspicuously failed to make anything of their own lives, they are naturally keen to ensure that their children's ambitions are similarly curtailed.

The school's brief prospectus reads promisingly, though the fact that it is written in strange, curly letters on pink paper should give uncommitted parents pause for though. They will search in vain for an optimistic message from the head teacher; the Spooner School has no truck with such elitist nonsense. All decisions are taken democratically, with every member of staff having an equal say in how the school should be run.

So even the simplest of matters - such as changing a tap-washer - requires the teachers to question the school's idiosyncratic philosophy, their place within it and the sacred bond of trust that binds teacher and pupil in a perpetual circle of something or other. The vote usually recommends a lie-down in a darkened room and the forming of a working party to search inside themselves for a unanimous answer to the tap-washer problem. It's a nightmare.

Small wonder that, unlike the parents, the teachers find any excuse to stay away from school. In how many other occupations would "bad vibes" constitute a valid reason for taking a day off work?

So what else makes the Spooner School different from other establishments? Well, the children are encouraged to get in touch with their feelings. This means tears and tantrums, of course, though that's usually the teachers. Since there must be no winners and no losers, competitive games are banned. Instead the children can enjoy peace dancing, painting badly and the celebration of arcane seasonal festivals. The school has declared itself a nuclear-free zone, which ensures that we in Milltown sleep soundly in our beds at night. And the children have school trips - whenever there's enough acid to go round.

The school lurches from one self-inflicted crisis to another. So thank goodness for our excellent 'after-school clubs' - more commonly known as amusement arcades. Here the kids have the opportunity to cadge cigarettes from lonely, maladjusted old guys in a pleasantly informal atmosphere.

32   Blame Someone Else

The government has acted quickly in response to our worries about British beef. Instead of mild concern we now have nationwide panic. So it's goodbye to beef 'on the bone' and hello to yet more over-priced, pre-packaged crap whose most wholesome ingredient is the sawdust sweepings from the abbatoir floor.

(A Doctor writes . . . "Lions are carnivores. While they may occasionally pick at a salad, what they really enjoy is raw meat. Cows, on the other hand, are herbivores, and their food of choice is grass. Not each other. Thank you".)

There is a quiz tonight at the Grievous Bodily Arms. The prize for the winning team is traditionally a navvy's breakfast. A heart-stopping plateful of sausage, bacon, liver, kidney, black pudding, spleen and spinal cord. There's not much call around here for tiny portions of food arranged seductively on hexagonal plates, surrounded by a little lake of raspberry sauce and topped with a sprig of parsley. What's wanted is some solid chloresterol that sends a man off to work with a lead-weight in his stomach and a giddy feeling in his head.

The pub's landlord is not a squeamish man. He only has his meat cooked because that's the simplest way to make sure it stays on the plate. He has a rabbit's foot hanging behind his bar. It's a lucky charm, though it wasn't so lucky for the rabbit, of course. It serves as a reminder that his views on animal welfare are delightfully uncomplicated. Hunting? "Foxes love it". Dogs? "Just for Christmas". Testing cosmetics on animals? "Jab the needle into that bunny's eye".

His thoughts on dietary requirements echo those of his pitbull terrier, that a proper meal needs plenty of red meat. True nose-to-tail eating: a man's meal. There shouldn't be much room on the plate for anything else. Vegetables aren't food, he insists. Vegetables are what food *eats*. When a hungry dog ventures into a shop, the landlord reasons, what is it likely to take? A string of sausages or an iceberg lettuce?

Well, it's his opinion, and not worth a bucket of warm spit, but he's happy to reprise it to anyone foolish enough to stand at the bar and feign even the slightest interest. But, in truth, this beef thing has got him rattled. After all, the quiz night regulars look forward to competing for a coronary-inducing trencher of red meat. As he wipes a rancid cloth across the bar-top the landlord wonders what he can offer tonight as an alternative prize.

The regulars at the Grievous Bodily Arms are an obstinate bunch, with unsophisticated tastes. Personal grooming is largely a matter of splashing raw alcohol into open shaving cuts, for the fashionable 'just out of prison' look. If they want exercise they'll hide the TV channel changer. Their idea of outdoor recreation is looting body parts from unconsecrated graves. Sex is for girls, they scoff dismissively. Anyway, they wouldn't know where to find a woman's G-spot; most of them would have trouble finding their *own*. In short, these aren't the type of people who will settle happily for a platter of low-fat turkey-style steaklets.

The evening news bulletin gives the landlord a flash of inspiration. He grabs a piece of chalk and, with a sigh of relief, scrawls on the blackboard. 'Tonight's Quiz: the lucky winners will enjoy two weeks on the Russian Space Station MIR'.

33   Man-to-man Marketing

The French have discovered that there's a huge audience for watching grown men fish numbered balls out of a velvet bag. Yes, it's the draw for the World Cup next summer, to decide who plays who. The commentators for this less-than-rivetting televised extravaganza wonder just how it is that the biggest teams are magically kept apart in the preliminary rounds. And how come France, the home country, are cosily grouped with Liechtenstein, the Faroe Islands and Rockall? After all, the balls look identical. But what would happen if half the balls had spent a few minutes in a freezer, with the other half in an oven? Just a thought . . .

It's approaching three o'clock on a Saturday afternoon, and Milltown's own football team is being cheered onto the muddy pitch by a few loyal fans. So few, indeed, that the team has been informed, over the tannoy, of changes to the crowd. It's a chilly afternoon in December. Older guys test the credulity of the younger fans by recalling the Ice Age ("Now that *was* cold . . .") when the arctic weather brought such chaos to the fixture list that the pools panel had to meet for three million Saturdays in a row . . .

Milltown Rovers are known in the league - the Vauxhall Cars Beezer Homes Sherpa Van Division (North) - as a sleeping dwarf. A club destined for mediocrity at best. With the team having spent years propping up the league, the club chairman decided during the summer that drastic action was required. When he swapped the entire squad for two bags of Cheesy Whatsits, local football pundits reckoned he'd got the best of the bargain.

The new crop of players have mostly been plucked from park football. Still unaccustomed to the luxury of real goalposts they have to be dissuaded from throwing their jackets down on the grass before the start of play. The captain picks his team in traditional fashion ("one potato, two potato . . .") which is why the scrawny players with glasses warm the substitutes' benches for game after game.

Other changes are afoot. The manager is trying to adopt the system of man-to-man marketing that has served Manchester United so well. The team's strip is now being sponsored, appropriately enough, by a local knacker's yard. To the question "How's the team performing?" there's only one answer: "Offal . . .".

When the sports reporter from the *Milltown Times* says that the players are "a good advertisement for the game", he is merely pointing out that they are covered from head to foot in sponsors' logos. Whenever they get injured, the players are contracted to crawl in front of an advertising hoarding, in case the photographer from the *Milltown Times* has remembered to put a film in his camera. Yes, the financial situation at Milltown Rovers really is that dire.

This is Milltown, so the club has a sports psychologist who works on the players' motivation. Nevertheless, when it comes to getting the required result, no-one's yet come up with a better method than locking the players in a small room and shouting at them. The bells at St Diana's Church are chiming three o'clock, so the pep-talk has to stop. Before taking his place on the bench, the manager cups his hands and bellows his final encouragement: "The grass is green, the paint is fresh . . . so get out there and bloody play".

34   Christmas Tears

Is sarcasm really the lowest form of wit? Surely not while Bernard Manning lives and breathes. But it's all too easy to scoff, isn't it? So let's see if we can find those rose-tinted spectacles - the ones we last wore when England were playing in the 1994 World Cup - and take a less jaundiced view of Milltown.

For those who don't know Milltown, just imagine paranoia in reverse: strangers smiling as they pass you on the street. Residents can either offer grateful thanks that they live in such a close-knit community . . . or complain that everybody knows their business. One thing's for sure: it's hard to keep a secret in Milltown. We do have a few smug bastards in Milltown - and the Smallholders would feel slighted to be excluded from their number - but they are still rare enough to be worthy of mention. As for the rest . . . well, we've already decided which is more important, 'quality of life' or 'standard of living'. In any case, our strict code of business ethics successfully excludes us from all the most lucrative areas of work.

Since almost everyone seems to live in an unpretentious terraced house, and drive a tatty ex-BT van, we are unlikely to be impressed by worthless status symbols. Such as money. We understand that a life filled with wealth would be a life of sham and shallowness. But just occasionally we yearn to discover, at first hand, exactly *how* shallow and meaningless such a life might be, so that we can then renounce it the more effectively.

The rows of terraced houses, giving straight onto the streets, look much as they did a century ago, when the mill-chimneys were more than just characterful landmarks. There isn't room to add on a conservatory, or a porch, or anything bigger than a satellite dish. We have to be a bit more imaginative if we want to make the neighbours purse their lips in envious disapproval. These are simple houses, eminently suitable for those whose lives are more concerned with 'being' than 'having'.

Taking its inspiration from the terraces of vines hugging the contour lines in a baked Tuscan landscape, Milltown has come to terms with its unusual topography. Imagine a washing-up bowl, with flat base and steep sides. Into the narrow confines of the valley bottom are shoe-horned the road, railway, river and canal. They cross and re-cross one another repeatedly, like the braided flex of an old-fashioned telephone.

So tightly are the houses crammed together that gardening tends to be confined to window boxes. They have character, these houses: a patina that can't be faked. Space was at such a premium at the height of the industrial revolution that houses were built on top of one another. 'Top & bottom' houses: what an ingenious response to a unique problem.

The rows of houses are stacked up the hillside like seats in a stadium, ensuring that most people have unhindered views over the rooftops of Milltown. As night falls, the bulbs on the Christmas tree in the square seem to twinkle ever more brightly. Through eyes moistened by tears the lights are surrounded by shadowy penumbra that dissolve with every blink.

Christmas is the time of year when we feel our own shortcomings most acutely. When the gap seems to widen, unbridgeably, between what we wanted to be and what we seem to have become. When we are forced to confront the goodness that's in the world and the badness that's in us.

It doesn't matter why the tears began. It could be the unexpected power of such cathartic emotions. It could be something as mundane as peeling onions. But for anyone standing, moist-eyed, by the window of a little terraced house in Milltown, those Christmas lights act as a powerful antidote against cynicism and world-weariness. Near the Christmas tree is a traditional nativity scene, assembled by local school-children: a heartwarming tableau of familiar figures that tell the Christmas story. The Virgin Mary watches tenderly over baby Jesus in his wooden crib. Joseph is protective, paternal, yet a bit dumbfounded by events he doesn't yet understand. Princess Diana, the first new recruit to this little entourage for almost two thousand years, peers doe-eyed over her surgeon's mask.

You could almost imagine that the garrulous trio of new-age travellers squatting nearby were the three kings - especially if they were carrying gold, frankincense and myrrh instead of cans of Special Brew. You know, once you put those rose-tinted glasses down, it can be the devil of a job to find them again.

35   A Tour of Duty

This is the day that the royal yacht Britannia is being decommissioned. The Queen has gone on board, one last time, to fill her handbag with light-bulbs and check down the back of the sofas in case any long-lost tiaras are still lurking there.

Most people are surprised to learn that Britannia has required a crew of 250 men to keep her running smoothly. For those who served aboard ship it was regular, well-paid work - like being the organist at Liz Taylor's weddings.

One minute the ship's crew were employed to cater for every whim of our pampered royal parasites. Then, suddenly, they're left high and dry, with nothing more to show for their years of fawning subservience than sea-legs and a P45. So there are a lot of people with specialist qualifications who are unlikely to find other work in their chosen fields. For example, what realistic hope can there be for the Inspector of the Royal Foreskin, as he forlornly circulates his brief CV to a shortlist of minor public schools?

Of course, this is not a question that preoccupies the shoppers of Milltown. With less than two weeks to go before Christmas, they are frantically looking for presents. It's a grim quest: to fill the void where Christmas spirit used to be with as much festive rubbish as their shopping bags can hold . . . and their credit cards can handle.

Charities, bless them, choose this time of the year to add guilt to the complex range of emotions already doing a frenzied tour of duty in our minds. There's quite an art to avoiding these tin-rattling do-gooders, while not appearing as tight-fisted as you really are. To deflect the guilt you need to adopt a facial expression that suggests: "Right on, comrade. I already give over-generously to a variety of charitable causes (including yours) but have a policy of not giving money on the street. Sorry". It's a complicated expression which needs to be practised regularly if it's not to look, to the recipient, like a bad case of constipation.

The shoppers' desperation to give their credit cards some serious hammer is good news for the retailers of Milltown. At the Twig Shop, for example, prices can be hiked to an unfeasibly festive high simply by going over the stock with an aerosol can of glue and a handful of glitter.

The record shop nearby specialises in music that nobody likes, which saves the constant hassle of ordering new stock. The shop window is full of CD compilations, featuring 'your sixteen soppiest love songs', with titles like *Summer of Love, Body and Soul* and *Heartbeats*. Then there's one called *All By Myself*. Who would have thought there were enough songs about masturbation to fill a whole CD? Town Drunk has bought a copy - for himself, appropriately enough. (Memo to record executives . . . Once you've raised the marketing stakes by issuing a CD entitled *The Best Rock Album In The Universe. Ever. Honest. No, Really,* how can you possibly justify the release of Volume *Two?*)

Further down the street is the Chinese take-away, the Wok of Ages, where hungry diners stand around for hours, drumming their fingers in frustration on the Formica counter. The only thing that keeps people coming back is to see if, just once, someone will order the advertised 'set meal for two'.

The Milltown Building Society next door has voted not to join the Gadarene rush to become a bank. It's somehow typical of Milltown that this august institution should have decided instead to convert into a delicatessen. There'll be no undeserved cash windfalls for regular savers, just a year's free supply of hummus and pitta bread.

Having nothing better to do, old folk queue stoically at the Post Office. Displaying the patience of grazing ruminants, they gaze myopically at the video screen above their heads, on which ageing actors extol the benefits of stair-lifts and commode chairs. Best not to be in a hurry, since the man in front of you will want to cash eighty-four postal orders, all for different denominations, before attempting to renew his provisional license to drive a three-wheeled, steam-powered road-roller. It's at moments like this that you wonder: how *do* they get second-class post to go slower than first-class?

There's a fleamarket every week in Milltown, where discerning shoppers can haggle over a variety of pre-owned treasures. You see stuff here that you just don't seem to find anywhere else: toasted sandwich makers, Polaroid Swinger cameras they stopped making film for twenty years ago, and LPs from the sixties with a mini-skirted dolly-bird doing the Mashed Potato emblazoned across the cover. And there's always an ancient Hoover with a sign reading 'Genuine Reason For Sale'. Yes, it's a genuine reason alright: it's fucked.

36   End of Innocence

It's said that everyone can remember exactly what they were doing when Michael Portillo contrived to lose one of the safest Tory seats in the country. Well, everyone except our Town Drunk, who generally has trouble remembering which way is up. Most other Milltown folk, blessed with the priceless ability to delight in other peoples' misfortunes, were laughing so hard that they became giddy and had to have a little lie-down.

After the general election, millions of triumphant Labour voters were punching the air like demented bit-players in a Coca Cola advert. But already they're becoming disillusioned. Reality is setting in, as predictably as hoar-frost on a winter's morning. The process of converting precious ideals into the base-metal of pragmatism takes most of us about twenty years, as life takes its toll on youthful dreams of a better world. The Labour government, in contrast, has managed the job in less than nine months.

With a speed that won't surprise anyone who has read George Orwell's *Animal Farm*, Labour MPs are casting their committments and pledges to the four winds. It's a convincing illustration that "whoever you vote for, it's the government that gets in".

What with the Tories asking the government not to cut benefits for the disabled and single mothers, and Labour ministers rivalling Marie Antoinette for capricious sophistry, is it any wonder the voters are disorientated? After all, suggesting that we can get disabled people back to work by cutting their benefits makes no more sense than getting them to walk again by confiscating their wheelchairs.

So thank goodness there's something that will unite us all, no matter which way we voted. Yes, the Millennium Dome, already taking shape on some God-forsaken meander of the Thames. It'll be enormous. Big enough, we hear, to hold two Wembley Stadiums, a notion which would make more sense if we *had* two Wembley stadiums.

Drivers of older cars will understand the sheer unalloyed excitement of watching the mileometer tick over from 99,999 to 100,000. This, in essence, is what we'll be celebrating in two years time. We in Milltown can barely conceal our indifference.

37 Festive Fare

We're cranking up for Christmas here in Milltown. The landlord at the Stoic has hidden the pub's collection of easy-listening CDs. His customers, already suffering from festive overload, will be 'entertained' by Christmas songs from the time he flings open the door each morning to the moment he locks it, with a sigh of relief, every night. A bizarre notion: that anyone sane would want to hear, yet again, Roy Wood's probably certifiable request, I Wish It Could Be Christmas Every Day.

There's none of this Christmas nonsense at the Grievous Bodily Arms. The pub has, not surprisingly, been declared a festive-free zone, and any tin-rattling do-gooders with the temerity to cross the threshold do so at their peril. Conversations with charity collectors or religious zealots tend to be brief and to the point. "Would you like a copy of *The Watchtower?*" "Would *you* like a ruptured spleen?" . . .

Yet even in a pub full of psychopathic malcontents, the landlord of the Grievous Bodily Arms is a man whose tastes for senseless violence put him in a league of his own. He'll happily regale his regulars with tales about all the Iraqis he killed during the Gulf War. Unfortunately he was living in Barnsley at the time.

"We only do it for the kids" is the clarion cry from the parents of Milltown, as they stack up their supermarket trolleys with booze. For eleven months of the year they warn their kids about the dangers of accepting sweets from strangers. Then, before Christmas, these same kids are taken to Santa's Grotto, and encouraged to sit on the knee of a portly paedophile with halitosis, a red outfit and a big white beard. It just goes to show that parents are the very last people who should have children.

The TV stations are going into overdrive, offering a festive cornucopia of 'Christmas Specials' and second-rate horror films. As though Christmas wasn't scary enough already. The schedules are building up to the cinematic crescendo that is Christmas Day. How strange that a

James Bond film - and the threat of world domination - is seen to embody the authentic spirit of Christmas.

'Tis the Season to be Frugal, tra la la la la, la la la la . . . So it's only right to pass on a couple of useful tips for those who don't like to throw their money away at Christmas. On the last dustbin round before Christmas, leave your rubbish with neighbours. The binmen will assume you're on holiday, thus avoiding the embarrassing face-off - and a dustbin emptied unceremoniously into your front yard - when you refuse to hand over a Christmas bonus.

And when the presents are piled up around the Christmas tree, economise by lobbing in some crumpled wrapping paper and a card. Everyone will assume that your present has already been opened, and will be too embarrassed to ask you what it was.

38   Sharp Relief

With a scarcity of hard news that isn't glittery and tinsel-wrapped, experienced politicos are on their guard at Christmas. So when the reporter on the *Milltown Times* phones our local councillors to check what they would like for Christmas, most of them have an anodyne quote to offer, such as "Peace on Earth", "Goodwill to Men" and "Re-open the public toilets". These irreproachable sentiments only serve to throw Councillor Prattle's wish-list into sharp relief. Given another chance, he'd probably come up with something more diplomatic than "A box of Havana cigars and a bottle of bubbly".

Christmas expectations seem to expand to fill about three months. But when does Christmas begin, and when does it end? It's no rhetorical question. When, for example, do people stop asking: "Are you ready for Christmas?" and start to wonder "Did you have a good Christmas?" Might there be a still point somewhere in the centre of the maelstrom - sandwiched between the Queen's speech and the last of the mince pies - when we are awakened to the true meaning of Christmas? Well, no, probably not. Best just to hope that the cumulative effects of booze, barbiturates and beef-on-the-bone induce a pleasantly pain-numbing narcolepsy.

(A Doctor Writes . . . Christmas only begins to make sense once you take a detached, clinical approach and regard the festivities as a strain of mass neurosis. Considering that most of us can't even organise a simultaneous orgasm between two eager and consenting adults, what realistic chance is there of 'Having Ourselves a Merry Little Christmas' all at the same time?)

The theory of relativity states that time passes more slowly when you spend Christmas with your family. The traditional turkey lunch is followed by the giving of gifts . . . and the exchanging of receipts. We cram ourselves into a single room, with only crackers, paper hats and a few games of Twister to keep us amused, and yet expect to come through the experience unscathed. It's unnatural to be closetted together so closely. Different houses would be good; different postal districts would be even better.

Even the most dysfunctional of families can be mollified by TV. Most of the films being shown over the holiday have the word 'Christmas' in the title, just in case we've been holidaying on Venus and hadn't noticed that the festive season had finally arrived.

To escape the horrors of Christmas altogether, Wounded Man flirted briefly with the idea of becoming a Jehovah's Witness. Until he realised he'd have to spend his spare time wearing nylon shirts and harassing people in their own homes.

After all these uncharitable thoughts it seems almost superfluous to wish readers a very happy holiday. But, as we raise a glass of something sparkly to 'absent friends', let's remember these wise words: "Love is never having to say 'Put that fucking axe away'."

39   Illegal Smiles

There are people in Milltown who don't know what it's like to spend a day without drugs. And you've got to admit that the Christmas holiday is probably not the ideal time to find out. By looking like they're on their way to a fancy-dress party, they make it easy for Dope Dealer to spot them. With his chemical stare, and indiscriminate 'flags of all nations' approach to drug-taking, he needs all the help he can get. Having selflessly road-tested all his wares, he's now blessed with the mental agility of a rocking horse. When he intones his mantra of available hallucinogenics his voice never rises above a parched whisper: "Dope, acid, speed; dope, acid, speed; spinal cord, oxtail, brisket".

The regulars at the Stoic may tut-tut disapprovingly. But pious pronouncements about illegal drugs are particularly fatuous at this time of year, when the yardstick for judging the success of Christmas seems to be the amount of brain-shrivelling booze they've manage to put away, and the size of the resulting hangover. "I must've had a good time; I can't remember a thing" is the happy conclusion to yet another orgy of over-indulgence.

The regulars at the Stoic will go further, reminding you that alcohol is legal, decent and honest, while cannabis is the spawn of Satan. It must be; it's illegal; it stands to reason. You won't get anywhere by arguing, but since when did that stop anyone? So here's a typical conversational gambit from someone whose drug of choice is alcohol, recorded anonymously during Happy Hour at the Grievous Bodily Arms: "'Ere, who are you fucking looking at? Wanna make something of it?" Compare and contrast with a typical greeting from a confirmed dope smoker: "Hello trees, hello sky". Enough said . . .

Life often seems precarious, like jumping from one slippery ice-floe to another. So it's good to take stock. The dawning of a new year provides a convenient opportunity to re-evaluate what's really important and what's just froth. After the usual roll-call of regrets and disappointments, Milltown folk look forward to 1998.

Willow Woman vows to become more assertive and less reliant on new-age mumbo-jumbo. At least, that's what the Tarot cards seem to be suggesting. Her daughter Sky will continue her fight for endangered species. After all, who else will stand up for nits and head-lice?

Since his ill-fated attempts to create an open-plan home environment, Biker Dave's little house in Hippy Street has lain empty. With the windows being boarded up one by one, as Christmas approached, it looked like an advent calendar in reverse. Now it's just a pile of rubble; a light breeze managed the job even before the demolition men could get there. So what Biker Dave wants most for 1998 is a place to live.

The barmaid at the Grievous Bodily Arms is becoming weary of trading shallow sexual encounters for small change. She's eager to regain her amateur status, in case casual sex becomes one of the demonstration sports at the Sydney Olympics. Instead of one-night stands she is looking for a husband: someone tall, dark and hyphenated. Failing that, she'd probably settle for a man with an IQ higher than room temperature.

Local Writer craves literary success. At a recent writers' workshop he was, sadly, the only writer he hadn't heard of. He isn't even a household name in his own home. If he was to have his time over again, he'd think twice before ticking the 'no publicity' box.

Our Tourism Officer is trying to push through a local bye-law compelling the men of Milltown to wear clogs, waistcoats and moleskin trousers, with pinnies and mob-caps for the women. He won't be satisfied until we're all just walk-on characters in theme-park Britain.

Mr Smallholder would like his applications rubber-stamped to join the Freemasons and the paramilitary wing of the National Trust. His wife can hardly wait for the January sale at the Twig Shop.

Wounded Man is less acquisitive and more reflective: a sort of spiritual gigolo. "You can't have everything", he acknowledges gravely, "where would you keep it?"

Town Drunk's wish for 1998 is much the same as it was a year ago. He wants a drink.

After yet another tour that has failed to set the musical world alight, the Uncles have bowed to public opinion: they've decided to reform as a Wurzels tribute band.

The Webmaster of Milltown's own little home on the world wide web is on a crusade. He wants to prove to doubters that the internet isn't, after all, just a cesspit in cyberspace filled with pictures of women having sex with ponies. This is why, in a probably mistaken attempt to go upmarket, the Milltown Web will soon feature women having sex with *polo* ponies.

40 Wet and Wintry

It's a soggy January, a bit of an anti-climax after all the festivities. The one hope, for over-indulgent Milltown folk, is that the hangovers will have subsided by the time the Visa bills roll in.

It's been raining for days. A photographer might enjoy the gilded reflections of street-lamps in puddles, and the way that the cobbles glisten in the back-streets. But everybody else sees just lowering skies and a succession of dreary days that makes summer seem a very distant prospect - whether you look forward or back.

The river, normally the most placidly turgid of watercourses, surges swollenly beneath the old packhorse bridge. Where it meets another beck, the water churns and bubbles like a cauldron of winter stew on the boil.

With the days being short - and the nights depressingly long - this is a good time for making plans and looking ahead. There's Lottery Millennium money available for creating new village greens, and Milltown is staking its claim. Councillor Prattle is confident that we shall soon have a new park to brighten up a neglected corner of town. To dissuade the kids from hanging around drinking cans of extra-strong lager and, incidentally, to create a modest tribute to Princess Diana's pioneering work, some - unspecified - areas of the park will be discreetly land-mined.

Willow Woman is browsing through the extensive 'self-improvement' section at the Milltown Bookshop. Despite already owning hundreds of titles that promise, perhaps optimistically, to "change your life", she can never resist buying a few more. Her current inspiration is an unequivocal feminist rebuttal of Transactional Analysis - entitled *I'm OK, You're OK . . . Now Piss Off* - which reaffirms her belief that there are few problems in life that can't be sorted out by a turn of the Tarot cards or a session of face painting.

She likes to get in touch with her feelings, to the detriment of other activities (especially housework). Exploring the innermost recesses of her own psyche can take an inordinate amount of time. There is no experience too meaningless, and no incident too trivial, to be related in its tedious entirety. So whenever you hear the dreaded words "I had this amazing dream last night . . .", you may as well sit down, plump up the cushions and make yourself at home. Yet the biggest question of all - "So what do you think? *Can* Man United do the treble this season?" - is the one she consistently fails to address.

It's an occupational hazard of living in Milltown for men to be told that they don't get in touch with their feelings . . . by women who appear to do little else. But any difference in attitude tends to be dispelled whenever there's an insistent knocking from underneath a car bonnet. Willow Woman's instinctive reaction is to don a pair of ear-muffs, hum tunelessly to herself while driving and hope the uninvited noise will go away of its own accord. When the car sounds like it could explode any minute, she'll invite some young buck to take a whistle-stop tour of what goes on beneath the bonnet. He'll be rewarded by a tray of inedible wholemeal scones, or a whistle-stop tour of Willow Woman, depending on her mood and the alignment of the planets.

It's simplistic to suggest that *every* Range Rover driver is an arrogant tosser. Simplistic, but true. Mr Smallholder likes to surround himself with the trappings of success. At work he has assembled a motley collection of time-serving lackeys. As he acknowledges: "Good friends may come and go, but sycophantic toadies are for *ever*".

Back at home there's his trophy wife, with her sun-bed tan and spendthrift habits. A significant rise in the FT Index might yet encourage him to trade her in for a newer model. But in the meantime he's content to be surrounded by servility; even his possessions have to know their place. He aims his key-fob at the Range Rover and presses the button. The lights flash obediently and the car gives a bleep that is reassuringly obsequious. "I am yours, O powerful one", it seems to be saying, "what might be your bidding?"

Pennine Pens: current list

A Little Bridge by Debjani Chatterjee,
Basir Sultan Kazmi and Simon Fletcher

(£5.95 and 95p p&p)

The Chess Board by Basir Sultan Kazmi

(£4.95 and 95p p&p)

The Occasions of Love by Simon Fletcher

(£4.95 and 95p p&p)

Audio book version (£4.95 and 95p p&p)

Me, Mick and M31 by Andrew Bibby
Children's environmental mystery (£5.95 and 95p p&p)

Sylvia Plath: Killing the Angel in the House
by Elaine Connell (£7.95 and 95p p&p)
A very readable introduction to the works of this great poet.

Presenting the Past: Anne Lister of Halifax
Jill Liddington (£5.95 and 95p p&p)
19th century lesbian landowner, traveller and diarist.

Cycling in Search of the Cathars
Chris Ratcliffe and Elaine Connell (£7.95 and 65p p&p)
This book about the "heretics" of medieval southwest France is
currently out of print. A full colour digital version is, however,
available for the Mac or PC.

Asma's Egg
Words: Chris Ratcliffe. Illustrations: Sean Creagh.
For children 4-7 (£1.95 and 45p p&p)

Details of our latest publications and
our **Web Design** services are on the Internet at
http://www.penpens.demon.co.uk

Pennine Pens, 32, Windsor Road, Hebden Bridge,
West Yorkshire, HX7 8LF. Tel/Fax 01422-843724